EXPEDITION HOME

EXPEDITION HOME

A JOURNEY TO SAFETY
FROM PANDEMIC INFLUENZA

THE PREVENTIVE QUARANTINE SOLUTION

BY SKIP HOFSTRAND, MD, PHD

Illustrated by Susan Seme

With an Introduction by Will Steger

Singing River Publications

Ely, MN 2006

ISBN: 0-9774831-8-5

Published by

Singing River Publications, Inc.
PO Box 72
Ely, MN 55731-0072
www.singingriverpublications.com

Author: Skip Hofstrand MD PhD
Pencil Drawings: Susan Seme
Introduction: Will Steger

Editors: Chris Moroni, Michael Wood, Karen Gravelle
Design & Layout: Michael Wood
Cover Watercolor Wash: Skip Hofstrand

Printed in Canada.

DEDICATION

To the billions of people who are at risk of death, disruption and debilitating illness in the imminent Pandemic. To the awakening of common initiative within community in preparing and living a preventive quarantine.

DISCLAIMER

The opinions and recommendations expressed in this book are those of the author and not necessarily those of any acknowledged experts or organizations. The general outlines of the potential pandemic influenza and its impact are being widely discussed and are roughly agreed upon by most medical and scientific professionals. The principles of Preventive Quarantine are less widely understood. The purpose of this book is to expose this common sense approach to a wider audience that may be interested in its immediate practical application.

CONTENTS

Dedication   *v*

Acknowledgments   *ix*

Disclaimer   *xii*

Introduction   *xiii*

Preface   *xvii*

CHAPTER ONE: 1918   1

CHAPTER TWO: THE GERM   9

CHAPTER THREE: PREPARATION   17

    A. Participants   20

    B. Homestead (Rural)   24

    C. Homestead (Urban or Suburban)   31

    D. Supplies   34

    E. Preventive Quarantine Community   37

    F. Pandemic Influenza Information Sources   40

    G. Sentinel Events   41

CHAPTER FOUR: ISOLATION   45

    A. Leadership   46

    B. Rules   48

    C. Specific Precautions   49

    D. Living Strategies   52

    E. Forays   57

    F. Communications   58

    G. Defense   60

    H. Fire/Police/Ambulance/Medical Emergencies   61

CHAPTER FIVE: AFTERMATH   65

CHAPTER SIX: PREVENTIVE QUARANTINE—YES OR NO
                                                        69

CHAPTER SEVEN: CONCLUSIONS   75

ACKNOWLEDGMENTS

Will Steger has always supplied camaraderie, expedition expertise and shared rural homestead living skills with me. I am grateful for his personal friendship and support—as well as for the introduction to this book. I look to Will for guidance with vision toward the hidden horizon. His polar explorations rank with the greatest explorers, and he has been accordingly honored. You now honor me, Will, on our Expedition Home.

I have drawn great medical inspiration from the Minnesota Pandemic experts: Dr. Michael Osterholm and Dr. Linda Van Etta. Dr. Van Etta has been a leader in disseminating information and warnings about the potential pandemic for several years—long before it became medically fashionable. Thank you, Linda. You are a true mentor, in every sense of the word.

I have been very appreciative of our "Preventive Quarantine Community" for their interest and support— especially Cathy Axtell and her husband Al, Sandra and Wayne Bennett, Ginger and Mitch Mesojedic, Jim and Geri Kangas.

Thank you to Gina Meissner for authentic, real experience, homestead advice and counsel. She is a wise lady who has trod the path of self-reliance for decades.

Jim Booth of Booth Associates has been my Pandemic Financial advisor. Many thanks to you, Jim, for your insight, expertise, and guidance.

Bruce Jessen is a close personal friend as well as a pharmacist who supplied information on medicines and sustainable living skills. He and his physician wife, Gail Baldwin, are "walking the walk".

Mick Seme, Sue's husband, has supported the project from day one and given incredible support and "backbone" to all of our efforts.

Louie Seme, now in his 90's, has contributed his personal recollections and living history from the 1918 Pandemic Influenza. Thank you, Louie.

Thanks to Tony J. Seme for his research on the pandemic influenza in Ely, MN, 1918.

Gus Gustofson has provided inspiration for the "natural order" and an incredible knowledge on sustainability and pure water.

Kudos to Geralyn Fernjack for the manuscript's initial typing.

And thanks especially to the wonderful staff of Singing River Publications: Christine Moroni, Michael Wood, Marjory Wood and Karen Gravelle, for their expertise and enthusiasm. Michael Wood's early guidance was instrumental in getting the project off the ground quickly. The wisdom of the others helped catalyze rapid publication.

And last, but far from least, to my art partner in Images of the Mind, Susan Seme. Her creative talent and artistic direction, as well as her home-making knowledge and skills, have been exceptional on this project. She and her husband Mick have molded all my efforts with enthusiasm and unbridled support. You are truly my heroes.

INTRODUCTION

Life on Earth is changing. The human race faces a number of threats: pandemic outbreaks, terrorist acts, global warming and critical energy shortages that make our way of life vulnerable. Our society, more than ever, is out of touch with the natural world that surrounds us. It seems that a general social and ethical malaise has eroded our common sense and vision.

To survive the challenges that lie ahead we must first become self-reliant. I have traveled tens of thousands of miles through the coldest weather on the planet and have come out on the other end in good shape and a better person. The key to my success has been in my preparation.

First, I must understand what I am up against. I am a good student and enjoy learning. Pre-expedition planning will find me in the library, searching on the Internet for information, talking to experts, and studying maps of weather, ocean currents and ice. I formulate as accurate a picture as I can of the region I am about to enter. If I am lucky, my route will take me where no one has ever been, so there will be many unknowns and plenty of adventure. As the study period comes to closure, I lay out an expedition plan. This plan will eventually be detailed - exactly to the level of required ounces of food, pounds of dog food, and gallons of fuel needed for the expedition. Detailed supply lists are blended with complicated logistics planning, ultimately giving me an accurate timetable and cost for the expedition. The success of each expedition is tallied on paper long before we set foot on the ice.

To survive the significant changes of an uncertain physical universe, we will need to become more self-reliant. The situation may seem daunting at first consideration. However, after considerable thought, several points become clear. We are dependent on complex systems, governments, and private and public organizations that may not be helpful in a time of crisis. What are we to do? First, we need to study the problems facing us before they occur. For instance, we need to understand just what a Pandemic is and to grasp the magnitude of it. With this concept in mind, we start our preparation for survival by laying out a strategy, creating action plans and checklists, and refining the small details.

There are also attitudes that have to be overcome. Some of our citizens would say, "This is doomsday thinking." I would say this is common sense. When I am faced with a potential danger on one of my expeditions, I will have prepared for it. Then, if it occurs, our team will be prepared to safely weather the storm – be it physical, mental, emotional or spiritual.

Preparing for a Pandemic, or for any other social crisis, means simply that we need to have an action plan and detailed lists. There may not be a need at this time to cash in our life's savings for gold, but it is well worth our effort to sit down now to study all the ramifications of this impending crisis and begin our action plan. The concept of Preventive Quarantine, so well detailed by Skip and Sue in this book, incorporates my thoughts exactly. Utilizing these insights, we can "ride over" the obstacles ahead. This could be the most important book you and your family read this year.

Will Steger[1]

---

1 *Will Steger is the 2006 Lindberg Award winner, John Oliver LaGorce Medal winner (National Geographic's prestigious award for exploration, science and public service—previous winners included Amelia Earhart, Robert Peary, Roald Amundsen and Jacques-Yves-Cousteau), and National Geographic's First Explorer in Residence Award.*

PREFACE

This book is not designed to be a treatise on the Pandemic Influenza, an infection soon to encompass the entire world on another of its natural cycles. There are many authoritative medical sources on the Avian Flu, which is the virus likely to mutate into the new Pandemic Influenza form. At the time of this writing this mutation has not yet happened. However, it is reasonable to expect that the Pandemic Influenza could begin soon. Just where and when is uncertain.

Pandemics are natural cyclic phenomenons that have typically had a major impact on the lives of humans all over the world. In this book I would like to provide you with a larger perspective on the problem as well as some practical information and advice on what you can do to keep this virus from harming you and your family. This perspective, and the preventive approach associated with it, is not based on fear, nor is it steeped in garlic necklaces, sauerkraut diets, or "survivalist" isolation from society in general. Preparing for Preventive Quarantine will permit you to physically isolate yourself and your family from the active virus for as long a period as practical, as a common sense approach to avoiding infection, sickness and death. Implementing it should reduce the load on health care services, lower the societal impact of the pandemic, and leave more people alive and in good health.

This book is specifically written for you, your family, and any friends or associates it may be feasible to be in quarantine with. It may also serve to extend the thinking or policies of governmental and business organizations, and other non-governmental groups, many of which are investing significant expertise and money in preparing for a pandemic —but that is not its primary purpose.

As a physician, I know the limitations that "common sense" advice and recommendations for preventative practices have in their ability to actually change thinking or behavior. However, perception of an impending crisis can, for some, serve as a "wake-up call". Hopefully, enough people will engage the approach outlined in this book, so that progression of the virus can be slowed, the load on essential health services lessened, and more of the sick can receive adequate treatment.

I truly hope the Pandemic will not materialize as the monster virus currently being discussed. I would like nothing better than to spend the next decade free of concern. However, my mindset is very much like Will Steger's—I want to prepare for future events that appear likely to occur, even if they lie in previously unvisited territory. Having prepared, I will cease to be anxious about them.

❧

Once the Pandemic begins, it will infect most humans in its direct path. It is during that time that you and your family need to be safely tucked away in the "preventive quarantine" that you previously prepared for. The common sense approach here is to avoid the disease by not exposing yourself to the virus. Just as the common sense approach to preventing yourself and your family from drowning in a flood is to get to higher ground before the water arrives.

For preventive quarantine to be the most helpful for you, you must enter it at the earliest feasible stage of a defined world wide Pandemic, when the World Health Organization announces it has begun. Your careful preparation prior to that time will greatly increase your chances of riding out the Pandemic with no illness or death. Thus preserving your health will lessen the load on critical health services and increase others' chances of survival as well.

Preparing financially may also permit you to continue to participate economically more than those that have not prepared and are out of work during the pandemic. Our social and economic infrastructure may be significantly impacted if the Pandemic reaches the predicted levels of morbidity and mortality. Preserving your health will make you more valuable in the re-building. Early physical isolation, or preventive quarantine, is a common sense solution to surviving this Pandemic.

The time in preventive quarantine does not need to be anguished or stressful. Depending on your circumstances, it could even be a pleasant experience. The length of the preventive quarantine that will most likely keep you free of infection will be in the range of four to twelve months.

A longer preventive quarantine will lessen the chance of a rebound infection from other population centers.

Since I have worked as medical consultant to many Arctic and Antarctic expeditions, I clearly see similarities between the preparation and execution of preventive quarantine and the preparation and carrying forth of an expedition. Since we are not going to Antarctica with dogsleds, "Expedition Home" seems an appropriate title for this book.

❧

For me, certain facts are clear:

1. There will be mutations soon in the H5N1 Avian Flu (or a similar Avian Flu group), currently spreading among birds, which will begin an unstoppable worldwide human Pandemic. Although science indicates that this will happen soon, we do not know if it will be this year or next, or even several years from now. However, it could just as easily begin tomorrow.

2. This Pandemic will likely begin outside of the United States, in contrast to the 1918 Avian Flu pandemic, which, based on our best epidemiological evidence, started in Kansas. Once the transition to human-to-human form occurs, the disease will probably not be contained. We have no medicines or vaccines at this time that will be able to control the Pandemic, nor is it likely to be contained by direct quarantine of those that first get sick. With today's high-speed transportation systems, the virus will spread rapidly

to all parts of the globe. An infected individual can board a plane and fly anywhere in the world before symptoms of the illness are present. Unfortunately, that person will still be spreading the germ during the approximately two-day symptom-less incubation period.

3. Once within the continental United States, the disease will spread quickly throughout all of our communities and population centers. Since none of us have immunity to this new pandemic influenza germ, those who are significantly exposed to it are likely to get seriously ill and have a significant risk of death. To get a sense of scale, consider that conservative casualty and mortality estimates indicate that this would be a greater disaster than a thermonuclear world war. Perhaps we have been de-sensitized by Y2K, which turned out, partly because of extensive preparation, to be less of a problem than was feared. Or perhaps we have been more recently sensitized by Hurricane Katrina, the most expensive natural disaster in history, which, with a few variations, closely followed predictions made for many years, but for which adequate preparations were not made. There are many potential problems in this world that can be quickly catastrophic: hurricanes, earthquakes, wars, volcanoes, tsunamis, and terrorist attacks. All have great potential for destruction. However, none would bring the level of devastation predicted for this new Pandemic Influenza.

4. Rich and poor, old and young, (and especially young healthy adults and pregnant women) all humans could get the illness if significantly exposed. The Pandemic virus

only slows and eventually stops when it has exhausted the human population in which it resides. No one is safe if you're in an environment where the virus is rich and spreading rapidly. Masks, goggles, gowns, gloves, hair covers, shoe covers and good disinfectant will be "temporary" barriers in significantly viral rich areas. Trained professionals may protect themselves in the hospital wards, but cannot let their guard down when exhausted and going for a cup of coffee at the hospital cafeteria. Individuals that have not been thoroughly trained in the techniques, and are not fully aware of the consequences of slip-ups, are much less likely to successfully maintain the discipline of barrier protection against the air-borne or surface-resident virus in their cities and towns. In 1918, health care workers on the front lines of the pandemic fell to the disease in greater numbers than any other group, despite the care they took to protect themselves.

5. The Pandemic Influenza is a natural phenomenon and you can use your common sense to deal with it. Common sense says, "Don't expose yourself to this germ". Once the Pandemic starts, you will not always know who is carrying this germ, or even what surfaces it may be on. Therefore, in order to avoid exposure to the germ, you will need to withdraw from physical contact with people or places where the virus may be active, for the duration of the Pandemic (except in short forays if you are thoroughly and effectively barrier protected). This is Preventive Quarantine, and it is the ultimate barrier technique—the one means you can institute to protect your family and contribute to the public health. Those who catch the disease will also "withdraw",

but they will do so with many more negative consequences, both to themselves and others.

Certainly, one does not anticipate being involved in an automobile accident when one gets into a car, but we fasten our seat belts anyway, just in case. If an accident does occur we are much better off thanks to our preventive preparation. Families preparing for preventive quarantine are putting on their "Pandemic seat belts". What you chose to do will depend on your circumstances and resources.

๛

The remainder of this book will give you an idea of what several families are doing. Although many of these families live in the "country," the same principles can be applied to urban or suburban living with certain modifications to the skills and techniques. The basic strategy will be disciplined withdrawal from physical contact with anyone or anything likely to be carrying the germ, the use of sustainable living practices and the application of love, humor and common sense.

Because it depends on social isolation, rural preventive quarantine is far easier than urban. For this reason, this book tends to focus on preparing for preventive quarantine in a rural setting. If your urban setting is difficult or impossible to isolate yourself in, think of planning now with rural families or friends. If this is not feasible, then creative planning can allow you to apply the principles and techniques of preventive quarantine in your city or suburban home as well, although it may be much more difficult.

Our Federal Government, and most State Governments, support local, rather than federal or state, approaches for minimizing the effects of the Pandemic. Preventive quarantine fits into this construct if applied at the individual, family, group or possibly community level. It may be possible, for instance, to apply Preventive Quarantine principles in preparing "places of refuge," utilizing schools, resorts, monasteries or the like. This requires a level of social understanding and cooperation that is beyond the scope of this book, but could and should be undertaken by those with the will to do so. Here in Minnesota, we are seeing the beginnings of this type of planning.

Preventive quarantine is basically an "all-or-none" process relative to separating yourself from the active virus. However, determining the sentinel events which will trigger the beginning or end of your quarantine involves a "relative risk stratification" process. In other words, if you enter the process early and exit late, your relative risk of contracting the disease is low. If, on the other hand, you enter the preventive quarantine late and exit early, your relative risk of disease and death is significantly higher. These are crucial decisions you will need to make. There is no absolute right answer—just the best answer for you and your family or group.

The preventive quarantine approach may give us a taste of what the future has in store with other, more slow moving crises, such as global warming and the depletion of fossil fuels. At that time, sustainable living practices will have to be the norm. Whatever you do from this moment on regarding these issues, please take the situation seriously, become knowledgeable about the pandemic and its potential, and then proceed with calmness and assertiveness to do what your common sense tells you is the right thing to do.

Skip Hofstrand

CHAPTER ONE:
1918

Frank Seme blew into his hands as he trudged to the Pioneer Mine for the morning shift[1]. It was a chilly fall morning even for Northern Minnesota. He was more than vaguely aware that the beautiful fall colors had already faded into the beginnings of an Ely winter. There was precious little time in his life to enjoy the wild beauty that surrounded Ely's "end-of-the-road" mining community. He and his family were poor. They were the forged products of immigrant Slovenian stock that had come to America to seek a new life. The Slovenian immigrant families and bachelor males hunkered down together near their only place of good work, the iron mine. The camaraderie of the Slovenian enclave was secondary to the importance of basic social communication. Although

---

1 *This is a true story gleaned from interviews with Frank's son, Louie, now 93 years old; as well as from articles in the 1918 Ely Miner newspaper.*

the children learned English in school, most of the adults remained stuck within their native tongues. In these poor ethnic sub-communities of Ely, where they were without electricity, telephones, radios or Slovenian newspapers the proximity of people of like kind was a necessity of daily life. This also meant that happenings in the world outside were just rumors, tales... distant drum beats that had no significance in their lives. World War I was raging in Europe, but was essentially unknown to them. Most were not United States citizens and were in no danger of being conscripted. Little did Frank know how this lack of accurate information would affect his life this fateful fall season—beginning this very night.

The entrance to his work at the Pioneer Mine through the "A" shaft was a temporary exit from the family part of Frank's life. Even though his beloved wife Margaret was pregnant, Frank had to put her, his two sons Frank Jr. and Louie, his small un-insulated frame house, his large garden, his cow, his pig, his chickens and his swaybacked horse back into the furthest recesses of his mind when he entered the mine. Here, concentration was an absolute necessity. The risks to life were enormous inside these timber supported shafts. The danger of a mud slide that could wash Frank and his fellow workers into a murky, thick, suffocating death always had a place in his thoughts, though hopefully never in the beam of his carbide lamp.

The incessant water seepage was a constant danger and a perpetual irritant. Frank knew full well the dangers of this mine. He had started in the mine as a dirt and timber "trammer" setting the supporting structures for the shafts.

He was hopeful of working himself into the enviable position of a "contract miner" who had a dependable salary as well as commissions based on production. His wife and he would often talk late into the night in the light of the kerosene lantern at the parlor table and dream of the better life that an increased income would bring.

Frank loved his family, but the ten hours a day, six days a week work schedule in the mines drained his 32 year old body so completely that he no longer attended the Saturday night dances. When he did make it to the Sunday morning services at St. Anthony's Catholic Church he often slept through the homily. Of course, he had not seemed so tired when he helped co-create their fourth pregnancy several months earlier. Margaret was a small frail looking woman who appeared much older than her years. She had experienced two easy pregnancies and then a stillborn daughter. This current pregnancy found her relatively healthy and happy. She kept busy with the cooking, canning, washing, mending, and cleaning. Tending to the rooms of the two miners who boarded upstairs was an additional chore.

The complete care of the two boys also fell to her. It was remarkable that she was able to keep track of these two active children. Frank Jr. was seven years old and Louie was five and both were in constant motion. They were old enough to be of considerable help to Margaret, though. Their main job was to keep the water buckets full by fetching water from the community spigot several blocks away. This was a never-ending chore. Of course they would rather have played with their friends than haul the heavy buckets of water, tend the animals, stack the woodpile or weed the garden. That summer, with a little help from their friends, they had even hauled railroad ties back to the house and cut them into firewood for the winter.

During their free moments one could find them engaged in practical jokes such as tipping over un-occupied outhouses, dis-assembling wagons and placing the parts on shed roofs, or pulling the fire alarms on the street lamp posts and running to a hiding place in the bushes to await the Ely Fire Department. They never complained about the work, at least not within earshot of their parents. A child just didn't do that here. Everyone worked as a team, like it or not. Little did the Seme family know that one of the four essential links in their team was about to be broken.

Margaret's illness started inauspiciously that morning, two days following Sunday services at St. Anthony's. It was remembered with accuracy because Frank had not attended services with her. This would haunt him for years to come. The kids had not gone either. Margaret told Frank on her return that the service was poorly attended because of a "flu-like" or "diphtheria-like" illness making many people very sick. Several severe diphtheria cases had occurred that summer. She felt the Sacrament of Communion was particularly poignant in that so many parishioners were ill and there was definitely a "Who's next?" atmosphere prevailing.

Margaret's influenza was most likely contracted that Sunday, because she had no other social contacts the previous week. Frank really never made the connection. He just felt guilty for not sharing her last church service with her. He would soon learn that what was happening to his pregnant wife was also happening to most of the other inhabitants of this "end-of-the-road" mining town and to communities and battlefields worldwide. This knowledge never lessened the pain.

Within hours of the first signs of illness, Margaret's body was wracked with pain and a high fever. A forceful non-productive cough kept her upper body in constant motion. The progression of her misery started after Frank left for work and was worsening when the kids arrived home from school in the afternoon. By then, Margaret knew she was very ill and she ordered the kids to go to a neighbor's house who had cared for them before. By late afternoon it became very difficult for her to breathe. She could barely speak to tell Frank to stay away from her when he arrived home. He usually followed her advice on such matters but this time his instinct was to hold her tight and to call Dr. Parker or Dr. Sutherland. Margaret convinced him they could not afford such a home visit. She lied to him, saying she would be "better in the morning." She was really thinking of her family when she claimed that she needed to be left alone.

Overnight her air sacs plugged with the rapid advance of the germ and her skin color turned a persistent blue-black. By the time the neighbor came by in the morning with Frank Jr. and Louie no one could recognize Margaret. She was dying in front of their eyes. An ominous pall descended on the kitchen where Frank and the kids struggled with the idea of leaving for the mine and for school. At this juncture, the schools had not yet closed and the mines had no idea of the horrible event that was transpiring in the community.

The mine operation was under orders to produce for the war effort and didn't tolerate anything less than full cooperation from its employees. No one wanted to leave but they realized there was nothing they could medically do for her themselves. Frank summoned the nurse hired directly by the miners for home visits.

Mrs. Kapch was much like a public health nurse. Her salary was supported by a three dollar a month deduction directly from each of the miner's paychecks. As soon as she arrived the nurse knew that Margaret was desperately ill with the illness that had already become a major community problem. She had already personally witnessed several deaths within the Slovenian enclave--deaths preceded by the very same progression of signs she was seeing in Margaret. Her only recommendations were strict isolation of the family from Margaret, a quarantine sign to be placed on the door and garlic necklaces to be worn by Frank and the children. Frank preferred his own "moonshine cure" to the garlic but Frank Jr. and Louie were so christened. Louie, to this day, can still smell that pervasive garlic odor with his exceptional 93 year old memory. He says he will wear another when this pandemic begins. He believes it was the garlic that saved him and Frank Jr. from the "scourge".

The quarantine on their home lasted only a few days after Margaret's death. During the early phases of the quarantine a policeman patrolled the streets on a motor-cycle making certain all the homes with quarantine signs obeyed the rules. It was somewhat of a pitiful joke since the adult males were still required to work in the mines. Frank Jr. and Louie were confined to their backyard and cared for by the neighbor.

The victims of this mysterious illness were buried as soon as possible to prevent the corpses from contaminating things. As the epidemic progressed and the deaths increased, the corpses soon overwhelmed the undertakers, grave-diggers, hearses and available cemetery plots. Although Margaret was in the first, smaller, wave of deaths, Camp Street often had two to three hearses a day "clip-clopping" to the new cemetery. Many more victims had to be stored in hidden cold recesses until help and facilities became available.

Drs. Parker and Sutherland from Shipman Hospital worked night and day. The hospital was soon overrun with victims, and Drs. Parker and Sutherland found themselves attending over a hundred home visits a day.

Not everyone died. Not everyone caught the germ. Those that escaped the disease were generally isolated families living off in the woods or families that, still healthy, intentionally quarantined themselves during the pandemic. This protective practice was directed, most often, by a strict mother or grandmother who ruled with an iron hand. The epidemic in Ely, as in the rest of the world, came in two waves. The first occurred in the late summer and early fall, and produced fewer deaths. Then, during the following winter and spring, a much more vicious and intense rebound wave occurred. This was the only year in history when the population of the United States was reduced from the previous year, rather than growing as it always has.

Margaret's death and the death of her unborn baby were unexpectedly rapid. She suffered significantly in her short struggle with the deadly pandemic germ, known today to be a strain of mutated avian flu similar to that which now faces the 21st century. The pandemic killed Margaret and crushed Frank. It crushed many. It altered the course of many lives and businesses in Ely and all over the world.

The Avian flu germ is presenting itself to the world again. Although we are better able to detect and understand it now, we are little more able to stop it than Dr. Parker or Dr. Sutherland were in 1918.

Louie, however, will confidently don his garlic necklace when he hears that the pandemic has arrived.

CHAPTER TWO:
THE GERM

Have you ever wondered what a "germ" really is? When we go to our physician with an infectious illness, sometimes we get antibiotics for "germs" and sometimes we don't. We get vaccinations for some germs and not for others. If you think about it, you probably know that germs are all over the surface of the earth and in the seas. Did you also know that they are the real farmers of this world because they prepare the soil for much of our plant life?

Germs are organisms so small that even a microscope may not reveal them. There are many types of germs. Some are more complex and larger and some can only be observed with a powerful electron microscope and are very simple in structure. Germs fall into one of five general categories: small parasites, fungi, rickettsia, bacteria and viruses. Examples in each of the groups are: the malaria germ, which is a parasite; the yeast germ, which is a fungus; the Rocky Mountain Spotted Fever germ which is a rickettsia; the strep throat germ, which is a bacterium; and the influenza germ, which is a virus.

The two types of germs we usually hear about are bacteria and viruses. Bacteria are one-celled microorganisms that can take several different shapes: spheres, rods, spirals and clusters. Bacteria are everywhere on the planet. They generally live outside the body cells of the animals, plants or humans with which they associate, or they live freely in the environment. Most bacteria are extremely helpful and are absolutely necessary to the cycles of life on earth. A very small percentage of bacteria can do harm to animal or plant life. Some of these produce human infections such as strep throat, pneumonia, bladder infections and cellulitis.

The symptoms of human bacterial infections are very similar to those caused by the other germs. Since the mid portion of the 20th century, science has developed chemicals, called antibiotics, which can actually kill or contain the bacteria and thereby help the body clear itself of a bacterial infection. Like all germs, bacteria mutate and evolve, thus developing their own defense systems. Over time, some types of bacteria have developed resistance to antibiotics, developing "super" forms of the basic microorganisms. This is becoming more and more of a problem because antibiotics have been used extensively in situations where they are not needed. This over-application has allowed the bacteria to get used to the antibiotics and mutate their genetic structure. Bacterial resistances are scary and troublesome and have our drug manufacturers trying to keep one step ahead of the resistant organisms by developing new antibiotics. Decreasing unnecessary antibiotic use would probably help more than anything else to bring antibiotic resistance under control. However, the germs will always keep one jump ahead of our technologies to control them. That's just the way life is.

Viruses are generally much smaller than bacteria and are considered "particles of life" rather than complete one-celled microorganisms. Some of the larger viruses look and act very much like bacteria. Viruses generally contain just genetic material (either DNA or RNA) and a protein coat. Most viruses need to invade living cells in order to complete their life cycle. They commandeer the host cell's cellular machinery in order to reproduce themselves. This is especially true of the influenza viruses. Viruses are ubiquitous and constitute the majority of common infections in humans, typically infecting the respiratory system or gastrointestinal tract. Any organ of the human body, however, can be involved in a viral infection. Viruses are responsible for the childhood diseases of measles, mumps, and chicken pox.

The symptoms of viral infections can be very similar to bacterial infections. Clinical judgment and specific testing often needs to be done to determine which type of germ is involved, especially since antibiotics won't affect the viruses. This is why your doctor, if he or she suspects a virus, will not prescribe an antibiotic for you. The great majority of viral infections in humans are self limiting and do not cause serious illness. One of the exceptions is the centerpiece of this book.

The influenza virus can sometimes be retarded in its growth by certain anti-viral medications (for example Tamiflu), but is more commonly controlled by vaccination procedures. Development and production of vaccines is a lengthy process which can take six to twelve months once a new virus is identified. Coincidentally, the process depends upon the availability of live chicken eggs, which could be in short supply if flocks are decimated by the avian flu. Vaccination will not be particularly helpful in the case of Pandemic Influenza because even in good conditions the vaccine cannot be developed in time to prevent the global spread of the newly mutated Pandemic strain. Availability of a new vaccine can, however, serve as a sentinel event to allow you to end your Preventive Quarantine.

New cellular based vaccine production techniques are more effective and productive than the current chicken embryo techniques. It is currently expected to take at least three years to develop this technology. Government assistance is needed to support this very important endeavor. At the time of this writing there is some interest in doing so on the part of the federal government in the US.

The smaller RNA viruses like Influenza can mutate and change rapidly because their basic structure is very simple. An RNA strand is one half the size and complexity of a DNA strand. The less dangerous annual influenza infections have a vaccine manufactured that is usually not specific to the Influenza infection of that year. This is because a guess is made the year before as to what the likely strain will be. The helpfulness of the vaccine varies depending upon how accurately the guess was made.

The influenza vaccine for the 2005-2006 flu season (and most likely for 2006-2007) contained an H1N1 ingredient, the same strain that caused the 1918 Pandemic. Because H5N1 is so different, and we have never been exposed to a pandemic form of it, the new pandemic influenza virus will meet little "resistance" in its sweep through the global population.

The influenza virus which is the motivating factor for this book has not yet mutated to its human pandemic form. What exists presently is an Influenza Type A germ called the Avian Flu, or more specifically H5N1, which has the significant potential of accomplishing this pandemic muta-tion. Presently the Avian Flu is a bird germ that has only infected human handlers of infected birds. These infected humans have become very sick, and approximately one-half of those humans known to be infected have died. The avian flu virus has not been able to spread easily from human-to-human however. It will need to evolve in order to accom-plish that. These infected birds and infected people have resided in foreign countries to this juncture. The fear is that the H5N1 virus needs only a small genetic change to mutate into the Pandemic virus which will then be able to rapidly spread human-to-human. Scientifically we know that the mutation to the Pandemic form is likely and basi-cally predictable, although, like other natural disasters, we can't foretell exactly when and where it will occur.

This H5N1 Avian Flu is a type of influenza called Influenza A. There are three general types of Influenza. The Influenza A strain, the Influenza B strain, and the Influenza C strain. It is in the Influenza A types of germs that we have the serious yearly influenza outbreaks. The more serious Pandemic form will also be a form of Influenza A. The H5N1 Avian Flu virus has been around, at least, since 1997 and has caused very serious illness when it has infected humans. The 1918 Spanish Pandemic Flu was also a mutated Avian Flu and its genetic structure has been recently ascertained from viruses extracted from Spanish Flu victim corpses that were preserved in the permafrost of Alaska since 1918. We have learned a great deal from this viral resurrection and from other new viral research. This information has all been applied to the present problem. The changes that occurred to mutate to the 1918 Spanish Pandemic Flu will likely be similar to what will happen soon with the H5N1 form. There is a possibility that this H5N1 mutation will make the Pandemic form less virulent and lethal than the present H5N1 Avian Flu infections in humans. (The present H5N1 Avian Flu mortality rate is approximately 50%). No one knows for certain at this time. What can be predicted is a highly virulent and lethal mutation which will rapidly spread from human-to-human across the globe.

There is little hope that anti-viral medications or vaccines will significantly affect this germ's pandemic progression. Nor will the early detection and early containment efforts by foreign countries be successful. These foreign efforts will, however, take place. From them, we will be able to know when the first phases of the worldwide Pandemic Influenza begin. Then we must brace ourselves for the impact. Hope resides in containment outside our North American borders. It is only a very remote hope.

This viral process is a natural phenomenon that has recurred throughout recorded history. Instead of fear or panic about its inevitability, consider using the common sense approach of isolation in PQ for you and your family. It is really the best personal defense system you have.

As Margaret Seme experienced in 1918, the Pandemic Influenza germ will be very contagious. It can live several days on dry surfaces. However, it is designed to spread through the air (airborne pathogen) with a cough or sneeze. If you don't breathe it in, you can easily become infected by transmitting it from your hands to your mouth, nose, or eyes. A more significant contamination, such as from a cough directly into your face, may allow the germ to take root more quickly and with greater effect.

The germ is uniquely adapted to being a "perfect infectious micro-organism." It works well as an infectious germ, and eventually "uses up" most humans in its path—then dieing down because there is no one else to infect. Ironically, part of its perfection as a contagion lies in the long incubation period and long course of illness—if it killed more quickly if would spread less effectively.

Most people who get infected live. However, for seven to ten days the disease is so incredibly miserable that the victims feel like they are going to die. In humans, there is an unusual feature with bird flu infections which we know occurred in earlier Pandemic victims. Many of those that die are young, healthy people in the prime of their lives. It is felt that the germ buries itself deep in the lung tissue, somewhat protected from the humans' early defense systems. It then stimulates such an intense immune reaction, that the reaction itself, a "cytokine storm," is the death-dealing agent. This severe reaction occurs more strongly in the young, healthy victims of the infection and explains the high death rate in these previously healthy victims. (Pregnant females have a very high mortality rate--victims like Margaret Seme and her unborn child).

This severe viral pneumonia resulting in death within several days of symptom commencement is not the only reason for the high mortality rate with Pandemic Influenza. If a victim has any serious medical problems (ex. heart disease) the overwhelming infection can put a deadly strain on these other organs. Additionally, there are many victims whose lungs weaken during the first week of the Pandemic Influenza, causing susceptibility to a bacterial pneumonia. These pneumonias are very serious, but are treatable with antibiotics if they are available. Of particular concern here are the growing number of bacterial germs resistant to the antibiotics normally used for treatment.

CHAPTER THREE:
PREPARATION

Imagine this... You've just come home from a long day at work. On the evening news you hear that in SE Asia, the World Health Organization has identified the beginning of the dreaded Pandemic Influenza. The newscaster states that the likelihood that it will reach the United States within one to two weeks is very high. The news report further adds that it is a highly deadly strain killing approximately 25 to 30% of those infected so far.

You realize that you've made a mistake in not preparing. You remember all the warnings about stocking extra food, so you immediately proceed to the nearest grocery store. You are unable to park in the parking lot because it is filled with cars. People are running to and fro with carts full of food. You get inside the store and find that there is little left to purchase, but you do get a few fresh supplies and canned goods that will last perhaps three to four days. Driving home, you're unable to find any other stores that are better supplied. The word has been out for several days, but you have not been listening to the news. You listen to the radio. The schools will be closing soon, public meetings are banned, and travel restrictions are planned by the state and federal authorities. You have heard of no plan at your workplace that would indicate what you need to do there.

Once at home, your family looks to you for direction. You explain that there are food supplies for a week if you all consume less than usual. From news reports, you know there won't be enough food to sustain your family if the Pandemic lasts for any significant length of time. Your feelings of dread and despair are contagious, and your family quickly gets caught up in your worry and concern. There is nowhere to turn for help. The majority of people in your community, and across the country are in equal disarray.

Hopefully, you and your family will never experience this situation.

The commencement of the Pandemic could have a totally different scenario. Had you learned what Pandemic Influenza is, what the consequences of being infected are, and what you can do to avoid infection, you might have been ready to meet this crisis. Perhaps you would have stocked enough supplies and made the necessary arrangements to enable you and your family to isolate themselves from infection during the critical period of this predatory Pandemic. Instead of dread and disappointment, you might be experiencing confidence and relief along with the commitment to fulfill the plans you had laid down before the Pandemic became a manifest reality.

"Quarantine" usually means that those that are sick, and contagious, are kept in isolation away from the greater body of people that are healthy. "Preventive Quarantine," in contrast, means that a group of healthy people are isolated from the greater body of people that are infected or likely to be infected. With the Pandemic virus, normal quarantine is unlikely to be of much use—the germ is too contagious and will be too prevalent. With Preventive Quarantine, however, small groups of people can be kept safe from the marauding disease as it sweeps through the greater population. If Preventive Quarantine were prepared for and practiced by a large number of people, then the course and speed of the Pandemic might also be changed. Any degree that the Pandemic can be slowed could give more time to vaccine production and help the delivery of essential services to the population

This book can act as a guide for you and your family. Understanding the Pandemic Influenza and being able to respond to it in an appropriate fashion with Preventive Quarantine is the aim of this book. To be adequately prepared, you may have to work harder than you ever thought possible and spend more money and time than you are comfortable doing. Budgets may need to be stretched to purchase needed supplies and put aside cash, relationships may be stretched as you discuss and argue about the implications of the Pandemic and the wisdom of your approach. Physical and emotional endurance may be tested as you put in the extra time to prepare and as you try to consider the scenarios involved in such an extensive disaster.

All of this work is useful, however, even if the Pandemic doesn't happen. The supplies you buy can be eaten and used. The preparations you make are useful for other types of disasters and changes. The knowledge you gain will give you better understanding, more resilience, and increased confidence in facing with many situations unrelated to Pandemic Influenza.

Your Preventive Quarantine will be as good or as bad as your preparation. As in any major expedition, preparation is everything. Preparation flies in the face of our present apathy, inertia and comfort dominated society. Most of us have become unable to be truly self-reliant. If you've had an opportunity to talk to relatives, parents or grandparents that experienced the Great Depression, you may not see this same sense of complacency in them. It may take something as significant as the Pandemic crisis to shake us back into a more realistic relationship with our Earth's human and non-human resources.

A. Participants

The participants in your isolated PQ will probably be family members and close friends. Participants should be selected, communicated with and decided upon in your pre-planning stage. All prospective participants will need to understand the Pandemic Influenza and its consequences enough to understand the implications of choosing to engage or not to engage in Preventive Quarantine.

This is your "cell group" for the duration of Preventive Quarantine.

The family needs to be very discerning when including others. If a possible participant in your PQ would be unable or unwilling to maintain the rules of your quarantine, the entire group could be jeopardized. Once relatives and friends hear of your preparation and desires, they may ask to be included in your cell group. It may be necessary to be very forthright and honest and perhaps suggest that they need to make plans to form their own PQ group, if you cannot include them.

The core members of your PQ must establish rules and goals ahead of time, and they must understand the need to adhere to them over the length of the anticipated quarantine. All participants who are capable of understanding the situation will need to pledge to the rules and guidelines of your PQ. Unlike many situations, adherence to the rules will mean life or death in this case.

A defined leader needs to be selected by some form of consensus or vote. In many cases, the choice will be obvious. An expedition also agrees on a leader, who will consider all options and directions for everyone. The rules and goals of the PQ must be irrevocable. This understanding must be strictly enforced during the entire journey into and out of isolation. Everyone must realize that sometimes the decisions made by the leader may not be to their liking, but nonetheless, the leader rules. This procedure works for major expeditions and needs to work for your Expedition Home.

Once your group knows each of the participants involved, calculations can be made to stock sufficient expendable supplies. Each participant may have special needs that need to be met. For instance, a disabled family member may need certain food, medical, or hygiene supplies. These must be stocked separately. If one does not know a participant well, that participant needs to attend to their own special needs or give adequate information to the leader, so the special supplies can be obtained.

The number of participants must not exceed the homestead, home or apartment's capacity. Each participant should have some sort of personal space, if that is at all possible. Personal space is key to the continued mental health of the group. The ability to foray in "people-less" areas will also help, but this depends upon the environment surrounding or adjoining the PQ site or reachable through available transportation and fuel.

Participants that have special medical or health needs, such as dental work or catch-up vaccinations, should attend to these issues as soon as they are chosen as a participant. Each participant should be responsible for most of their own special needs. For example, an adult on medication should be responsible for going to their physician and obtaining adequate amounts of their prescriptions beforehand. The costs could be "out of pocket". Each participant, as they are financially and physically able, needs to contribute to the expendable supplies.

There may be family members or friends or distant relatives that arrive unannounced, who were not part of the initial planning or selection process. There may be other potential participants who are just not certain when asked what they want to do. It is the job of the leader to make certain these people understand that once quarantine starts, they will not be allowed to come into the isolated facility if they have not been planned for. Decisions will have to be made beforehand, and then held to firmly, despite the possibility of hard feelings.

If the possibility exists that somebody will *likely* join the Preventive Quarantine once the pandemic occurs, even though they are indecisive or non-committal now, then the PQ group needs to plan their supplies including that person or persons.

The arrival of someone whom you wish to have enter the quarantine, after the quarantine has begun, will need to follow a specific process. This means that for a period of seven to ten days the new arrival resides in some sort of separate facility in or near the home or homestead, so that it can be determined whether or not they have contracted the virus and could be bringing it into the Preventive Quarantine. During this period, the new arrival(s) is not in contact with the outside world, and also has no direct physical contact with those in the PQ. If no flu symptoms have manifested after seven to ten days, they can then enter the secure PQ unit. The primary objective of PQ is to avoid exposure to the virus. Once the pandemic has begun, this means avoiding contact with *anyone* who is not *known* to be virus-free, or any surface that *could* be contaminated with the virus.

For cases where contact is unavoidable, the use of barrier equipment and techniques (mask, gloves, goggles, gown, hair cover, shoe cover) should always be immediately accessible to all participants.

B. Homestead (Rural)

Depending on your circumstances and resources, the environment for Preventive Quarantine may be rural or urban. The rural homestead is obviously a more suitable place for such an endeavor. Sustainable living practices are more easily carried out in such an environment. If you are living in an urban or suburban setting, your best strategy may be to find a rural retreat spot, rather than ineffectively attempting to structure the PQ space within an apartment building or neighborhood. However, you may not have that option. In that case, your creative planning must begin early and you will need to be ready to practice greater discipline under more strenuous, difficult and limiting circumstances.

Modifications of the rural homestead may be necessary prior to the institution of PQ. These modifications would be consistent with general sustainable living practices, and could be well-utilized after the Pandemic Influenza is history. These modifications may include the institution of backup systems for heat delivery, food storage, water procurement and storage, human waste disposal, lighting, food preparation systems, and food production systems. These backup systems are required because energy systems and societal services may be disrupted during the pandemic.

Because of their vital influence on survival, heat, water and food specifically have to have alternative sources of supply. In an ideal PQ, these systems would have two backup sources. For example, if one were using electrical heat, establishing propane and wood backup systems could be appropriate. If there is a community water supply system, it could be backed up with storage, a well, and/or rain water collection. If there is a residential well water system with an electrical pump, the electrical system will need to be backed up with a gas generator, or a hand pump could be added, if feasible. Food can be stored, or can be grown in gardens, green-houses or even in window trays or deck boxes. All the solutions are extensive and expensive and go beyond the simple concept of storage. Ingenuity may provide some additional answers. One does not want to be caught without resources in the case of extended power outages, disruption of community services, or disruption of other energy supplies.

If someone in the cell is a skilled worker, some of these backup systems could be developed during PQ, provided the necessary supplies, tools and equipment have been stocked. If not prepared ahead of time, there is the risk that they will not be ready when they are needed.

Food storage ought to be thought out in advance. You do not want to lose a large portion of your food supply through spoilage. The electrical system supplying refrigeration could be supplemented with generator power. That would require a considerable amount of fuel and might not be practical. It may be wiser to stock food stored in cans or other means of dry storage, making refrigeration a non-issue. Properly stored dry bulk commodities should provide at least half of your projected food supply.

Dry food storage, such as rice, wheat, corn and beans, needs to be protected from the weather and from rodents. It may be stored in a secured storeroom or basement where it can easily be monitored. Canned foods need space and also shelving capable of holding the weight. The types of foods used by any particular PQ group may vary according to specific taste and nutritional requirements, and will also be influenced by financial considerations. Bulk dry food fits well with these considerations.

When food is in short supply, or some type of rationing is being done, pilfering from within your group could become an issue. A storage facility that allows for security of the food supply could be quite helpful. Because each homestead/home is unique, specific ideas for backup systems should be tailored to each particular sight. It's obviously very difficult to make modifications in a very short period of time when the Pandemic is bearing down. It is easier to make modification plans when they are considered to be part of a broader and longer-term plan for sustainable living.

Although gardening would be nutritious and a helpful supplement to stored food supplies, do not depend on that source. For some homesteads, gardening may be a source of joy and food already. For a beginner, gardening is too undependable for food, although it may be an excellent way to decrease stress and find joy. Any food produced can be a bonus to stock provisions.

The ability to have productive gardens, and to hunt and fish, can provide additional benefits, as can food smokers, dehydrators, and canning systems. However, these should not be relied upon as anything but additive features for your food system. Food needs to be protected from heat (70 degrees or cooler) contamination, sunlight, moisture, rodents, and insects. Special measures to retain nutrients in food need to be taken if long quarantine times are anticipated. Do not throw away spoiled foods; add them to your garden or compost.

A root cellar would be an excellent storage facility for certain food types. Perhaps it is beyond the scope of the average PQ, but it certainly fits the long term sustainable life style.

It cannot be emphasized enough to have personal space for individuals in the quarantine. Virus-free natural environments, such as forests, woods and lakes, will also preserve sanity. As time proceeds, stress will be a factor which will compromise survival, and will undoubtedly play a big role in the situation. Preplanning for fun activities, hobbies, videos, DVDs, books, games, etc., will be positive diversions. Children will have to be emotionally prepared for what is facing them. Love, reassurance, and attention will always be the right strategies. Get them involved early in procedures and fun, as well as responsibilities. Pay attention to them. Good parents do these things automatically, but remember that parents will be under their own stresses. Children unprepared for the quarantine will be a major quarantine disruption, although they are often more adaptable than adults!

Television and the Internet may be available during quarantine, and are a good way to stay in social contact while sustaining physical isolation, but they may also be disrupted for periods of time. Similarly, phone and cell phone systems may also be intermittent.

Planning for disposal systems is necessary. Garbage, latrines for human waste, and the possibility of dead bodies are the areas of focus. Hopefully, deaths from the Pandemic Influenza will not be a problem in your group, but rather the possibility of death from other sources. It may not be possible to leave quarantine to bury the dead, so provisions will need to be made within the scope of your quarantine.

There may be a need for additional storage of fuel, kerosene, and extra water. Oil or petroleum fuels will slowly oxidize over time producing sticky gums. Ethanol fuels do the same. These gums plug small openings in stoves, engines, or furnaces. Stabilizers and similar additives are necessary for storage. Kerosene is less problematic, since its substances have been removed in processing, thus extending its shelf life without the additives. Calculations regarding supply may not be accurate, so overestimating your needs can be helpful. Although water can be collected from roof systems, streams, lakes or snow to supplement needs, fuels cannot be generated in the same fashion.

Lighting systems need be considered, especially in wintertime when nights are long and the possibility of power failure exists. Battery backup systems will be helpful, as well as kerosene systems or other lamp systems that give enough lumens to prevent cabin fever. Some lamps burn isopropyl alcohol and do not emit odors or carbon monoxide (do not underestimate the danger of carbon monoxide). Also, do not underestimate the need for good lighting systems, especially in winter.

Extra space can always be utilized for many things. In summer, a functional screen house could be a popular feature. In the winter, closing off rooms with blankets or plastic sheets to conserve heat in a core area can all be planned in advance. In addition, warm clothes, blankets, and sleeping bags will be necessary if and when heating becomes an issue. In the summer, obviously, there is less of a problem with clothing and blankets.

On the grounds of the homestead, a holding trailer(s) or large wall tent(s) could be used for additional facility needs for the quarantining of a visitor that may arrive. As described above, this individual needs to be away from the group until it can be ascertained whether or not they are carrying the disease.

The PQ unit may wish to have communication systems available beyond the usual phone, radio, TV, cell phone and/or Internet. Satellite phone systems may be the most consistent, but are expensive. Cell phones have not had a good record in major catastrophes such as 9/11 and Katrina, although in this case there should be little, if any, damage to the physical communications infrastructure. Ham radio operators are usually life-lines in severe situations, but this means of communication may not be practical for individual PQ units, as it involves equipment, training and licensing. Walkie-Talkies can be useful in certain PQ forays, or between different PQ households.

Pets may need new rules. They should not be allowed to run free. Kenneling or leashes will be necessary, as pets should not be allowed to leave quarantine areas. Dogs or cats invading your PQ may be contaminated and could be very dangerous as carriers of the germ. They may have been the close companion of a dying Pandemic Influenza victim.

If the homestead bicycles and other non-motorized means of transportation have not been greased and oiled, they should be made ready for extensive use. Under certain circumstances, well-defined and controlled forays from quarantine may be necessary. In certain rural homestead localities, natural food gathering might be expedited by non-motorized vehicles. Since fruits and berries, fish, and appropriate wildlife can extend food supplies and provide variety; the homestead should have fishing equipment, snares, traps, and other means of gathering wild produce.

A rural homestead is an ideal place for the self-sufficient approach to PQ. Despite its many advantages, it will still need adequate preparation time and financial investment to procure and maintain many of the backup systems. If we are so lucky as to have the Pandemic delayed for one to two years, these investments and changes will be easier to accomplish. We can only do the best we can do. Every homestead will have its own particular gifts, as well as needs. I know of many places now that are already able to carry out a year-long PQ without the addition of any new systems or supplies. These families have been practicing sustainable living for many years.

C. Homestead (Urban or Suburban)

In some situations, urban dwellers may seek to prepare their Preventive Quarantine in a rural area with friends and family. Many people will not have their choice of urban or rural residence, however, or may choose to stay in an urban setting.

It seems that staying physically isolated and safe in an urban home, condominium or apartment while the pandemic rages through your neighbors will be greatly challenging, to say the least. Those who undertake urban PQ may choose to reduce their PQ time because of the difficulty of maintaining physical isolation or of storing sufficient supplies. This will increase the risk of infection. Certainly the risks for infection, despite precautions, will be much higher in the urban environment than they are in less densely populated rural settings. It will be harder to maintain strict rules where there is constant proximity to numerous potential viral sources. The temptations to break the rules and compromise the quarantine will be numerous and strong. The urban environment, as we have seen in other disasters, is also more likely to have social unrest, looting and desperate people with weapons.

Brainstorming and scenario planning during the preparation time will be essential. Modifications and innovations may need to be essential parts of the preparatory time period as you work out the unique physical, emotional and social challenges of urban quarantine.

Creative systems, such as backyard gardening or earth boxes for food production on the back deck, might provide additional food choices. With enough stored automobile gas, careful forays with very careful contagion precautions could be possible. This would involve special techniques for protection in viral rich environments. Full barrier equipment and techniques, depending on the situation, may be necessary. After the foray, masks and gloves can be destroyed, and gowns appropriately washed using a water and bleach solution (9:1 water to bleach ratio).

In the urban setting, food supplies will generally need to be canned or dry. The choices depend on taste, space, and resources. Bulk items (such as flour, rice, peas, beans, sugar, etc.) will provide for basic nutritional needs over a longer period of time, and can be stored in less space. Gardening in the backyard, in earth boxes, on the deck or on a roof could be valuable, but perhaps undependable food sources. Just as in the rural setting, consider gardens a potential supplement, rather than depending on them for essential nutrition. Additionally, a bread maker with adequate amounts of stored ingredients could help keep you safe at home and keep depression off your shoulders.

We don't know how vulnerable city and town water supplies will be during a pandemic. Certainly, storage of as much water as you can is a good standard. Recommended survival amounts for drinking are eight gallons per adult per week. Water for hydration will be more important than water for hygiene. Moist wipes can be used for some hygienic needs. Remember that hot water tanks have relatively clean water that can be drained. Human waste disposal can be accomplished by strong plastic bags rather than flushing. Flushing can be reduced to a few times per day, especially for only urine. Composting toilets may be feasible in an urban setting, but we have not studied this.

Many systems will not be able to be backed up, but are dependent on the larger urban systems for energy and power. If these fail, camping equipment may need to be used for cooking and heat (be especially careful if camping equipment is used for indoor heat or cooking--always follow manufacturer's recommendations for safe operation). Additional clothes, sleeping bags, and blankets can reduce the need for heat in the winter. However, staying cool in the summer will be problematic if there is a lack of air conditioning.

If sleeping quarters are tight, sleeping in shifts may need to be instituted.

With a longer planning time, such things as solar panels or even wind generators could be installed for key electrical needs, unusual as these might be in the urban setting.

In summary the urban homestead will be a challenging place to set up quarantine. But, with adequate planning and creative thought, PQ can be accomplished in the urban environment.

D. Supplies

Three of the most important elements of preparation are

1) determining the supplies needed,
2) acquiring them, and
3) repackaging and storing them.

This is expedition planning exemplified. To begin, certain calculations are necessary. These calculations include the number of participants in the Preventive Quarantine, the projected quarantine time, and modifying factors. It would be best to calculate quarantine time for the longest possible duration. This will vary with your situation. If the time turns out to be less than anticipated, you are not in trouble with the extra supplies.

Modifying factors may include eating less, using less product, and lengthening certain time frames. If one normally washes clothes every week, one could wash clothes every two weeks (except for decontamination items). If one seriously considers these types of modification, considerable extension of financial savings, space, and food supply can occur. Urban quarantines may benefit from these modifications the most.

We can get along for long periods of time (some of us better than others) on very little food for maintaining vital body functions, but we cannot get along without adequate amounts of water. *Think seriously about water, how to get it, and how to store it!*

The general categories of supplies are:
- food,
- water,
- fuel,
- expendable products,
- essential tools and equipment,
- over-the-counter medical supplies, and
- prescription medical supplies.

Lists of recommended items in each of these categories are delineated in the Appendices.

Prescription medical supplies are of two types. The first type is any prescription that you or your family members take regularly. The second is a list of prescription medications that your physician would recommend that you have on hand in your PQ for emergencies. If possible, each participant should provide their own medical supplies. Each should seek the advice of their physician as to whether they really need the medication they are taking, or whether they can cut back on the amounts or go to a less expensive alternative. Obtain the medical prescriptions through insurance, if possible, but be prepared to pay for 3-6 months worth of prescriptions out-of-pocket. If the PQ is run correctly, there should be no need to care for Pandemic Influenza victims in your cell group. While a supply of Tamiflu may still be helpful, if it is in short supply it may be better to let it be used by those who need to treat the sick outside of PQ.

Propane tanks of many sizes will be helpful if propane systems are used. Gasoline and kerosene storage are also important if your equipment needs these fuels. All fuel systems need to be inventoried and maintained regularly. Special fuel allocation for foray trips could be a "God send."

Expendable supplies must also be inventoried regularly. This will allow for better distribution and utilization of the supplies during the remaining time. It should also discourage scavenging or pilfering by participants. Pets need to have their food supply as well. Don't forget your pets. They will provide a measure of sanity during long quarantine hours. Pet diets can be supplemented by table scraps and other left-overs.

Especially important in household supplies are the paper products. This includes toilet paper and paper toweling. Can you imagine running out of toilet paper? It has become a necessity along with food, water, and heat. Newspapers, catalogs, and other recyclable paper can be used if necessary, although not the slick surface papers. Be certain not to flush this paper, since it will clog plumbing pipes. Instead, dispose of soiled paper in plastic garbage bags.

Lists of expendable and non-expendable supplies are listed in the Appendix.

E. Preventive Quarantine Community

The cooperation and coordination of several individual homesteads, homes or apartments involved in Preventive Quarantine, each following the same rules, allows for a supportive community. Proximity allows a greater degree of interaction. Although not absolutely essential to the effective single PQ unit, a larger community provides certain advantages to any participating unit. Essential to forming such a support community is the absolute commitment to the isolation from physical social contacts that could bring the virus into any part of the support community. The formation of this larger community can be done at any point in the pre-planning or planning stage, but it cannot be done casually and will require the establishment of trust and respect between the individual cells. In certain cases where resources or skills are going to be shared between cells a larger governance structure that spans all the cells may be useful or necessary.

Meetings and get-togethers of potential community members which clarify the understanding of the pandemic and the implications and dangers thereof, need to happen early in the planning stage. All questions need to be answered so that all participating units can comfortably agree to the rules. Each separate homestead needs to trust the other units and to keep an eye out for each other. The support communities should be within walking or biking distance of each other, if possible. If there is the facility to store gasoline, or it is available otherwise, support community units could be farther from each other.

A big plus for individual homestead/home/apartment participants is to have access to people with many different types of basic skills. In the most severe periods of the Pandemic, there will likely be little ability to call for outside services. Even if services and personnel are available, the danger of inadvertently bringing the virus into the community is great. Every participant will bring a different set of skills to the PQ community. These should be discussed at early meetings so that each participating homestead will know which skills are available to the entire community. The best way for this system to work is to have everyone agree that all services provided are of equal importance and value. For instance, a plumber's skills will be of equal value to baby-sitting skills. A list of people with relevant skills and their corresponding contact information should be made available to the entire community and should be posted at each site.

At these early preparatory community meetings, expectations must be set and rules defined. Although any individual unit may have their own needs and desires, a successful PQ community must have every participating unit pledge to the rules determined by the group. This is vitally important. Exposure to outside people, deliveries, or mail, could bring the virus into the community, as could improperly handled forays, or a family member wanting to come in late. Accepting entrance for such a person or people might be an individual homestead decision. However, everyone would need to agree that people entering from the virus-rich environment would have to have their own quarantine in a separate trailer for seven to ten days before entering the unit, as described above. Cell groups unable to agree to this process will need to fashion their own plans with their own risk stratification. They cannot be a member of the PQ community.

Besides support for projects and repairs, the community group will also provide stress relief for each other by having fun get-togethers. These could include potlucks, music concerts, book clubs, rummage sales, group movies, or dinners and picnics. The individual group leaders of each participating unit will meet on a regular basis to make certain everyone is abiding by the rules of community and to plan fun events together. Luckily, no barrier techniques are needed for these events, since all have followed the PQ rules. Discussion about any information recently learned from the outside environment will also be addressed. The community could also participate in mutual aide for fire protection and police or medical services that will likely not be available during pandemic onslaught.

In the preparation phase, the support community should keep their specific information within their community. Meeting regularly, the leaders should discuss everything from the movement of pets to the confirming of sentinel events.

It doesn't take much imagination to envision a truly functional supportive community becoming the basis of a future sustainable society.

F. Pandemic Influenza Information Sources

To be able to understand a pandemic and its potential devastation, one needs to have trustworthy and dependable information sources. Since most federal and state agencies are supporting local approaches rather than conducting supportive activities themselves, much planning will need to be local and either family or community based. If your state or country is an exception to this, as Minnesota is to some degree, then you can track down their sources of information, planning and coordination.

There are two basic and trustworthy information sources for accurate factual information on the Pandemic. These are the Centers for Disease Control (CDC) in the United States, and the World Health Organization (WHO). Their web sites, at www.cdc.gov and www.who.int, can be easily accessed through the Internet. The relevant US government site is www.pandemicflu.gov, and is a good source of information, along with the CDC site, on activities and preparedness in the US.

The Latter Day Saints Religious Group (www.providentliving.org) is expert in sustainable living practices. They maintain their required one-year supply of food and other supplies. Their web site contains helpful information regarding these issues.

If you look, you will find numerous other sources on the virus, its progression, sustainable living and other relevant topics online, as well as other books and articles that are available.

In the long run, our best helping hand is at the end of our own arm. Our local meetings and individual planning for Preventive Quarantine will bring forth our best solutions to quality survival. The PQ community is a gathering in which information from all sources can be shared, discussed, and evaluated.

G. Sentinel Events

A "sentinel" is a guard, one who watches out for approaching danger. A "sentinel event" in medical usage is a rare or unusual event, especially insofar as it violates standard process, that leads to a particularly bad patient outcome. In our usage, we simply mean an event that signals us to take particular actions, such as entry into Preventive Quarantine.

A likely sentinel event for many will be the WHO's announcement that the active influenza virus has attained efficient and sustained human-to-human transmission, or Phase Six of a pandemic alert[1].

The early agreement on which events will trigger our entry into quarantine is a critical element of the overall PQ plan. Specific sentinel events may be considered more or less important by individual communities. These

1 A chart with the defined pandemic phases from the WHO can be found at www. who.int/csr/disease/avian_influenza/phase/en. At the time of printing we are at Phase Three.

sentinel events need to be crafted and understood from the best information available. You may choose different sentinel events for several different withdrawal strategies. For example, there may be a sentinel event to take one's children from the public school system. There may be a separate sentinel event to trigger withdrawal from restaurant contact and any public meetings or shopping excursions. There may be a separate sentinel event for one to exit the workplace. There may be a separate sentinel event to know when to begin enforcing seven to ten day trailer quarantine. And finally, there may be a separate sentinel event to withdraw money from the stock market or similar financial institutions, if you have decided that this is an important thing to do[2].

All of these features of withdrawal may be done simply with one sentinel event, such as the announcement by the World Health Organization that the definition of pandemic has been met, though it has not reached the shores of the United States. Someone else's single sentinel event may be the first proven case or cases in the continental United States. For others, it may be the announcement of "containment" practices at the site in a foreign county where the Pandemic virus has been proven and is readily moving from human-to-human. If the scientific predictions about the rapid spread of the virus are correct, the practical differences between physical withdrawal at the time of the WHO Phase Six global pandemic alert versus

---

2 *One needs good financial advice from an advisor who understands the issues. Some have a predisposed notion that nothing will go seriously wrong with our economy. Seek good advice early.*

at the time that the first infections are seen in the US will be negligible.

Sentinel event decisions need to be discussed with your work place, your children's school, your church, and any other social gathering spots. None of the social exits will be easy, especially at the earlier stages. However, if all the economic and medical projections are correct, it will be just a short time before there would be forced withdrawals anyway, because of illness, care for others, or workplace closures.

Since everyone may have different information on pandemic issues, have prepared differently, or have different financial needs, some people may choose totally different approaches to exiting or remaining at their job. Some jobs may be continued at home, or be conducted virtually over the Internet or by phone. Some work places may give excellent barrier protection at the job site and make the risks less for remaining at work, provided the travel to and from your work can be done with adequate protection. Some jobs may be considered absolutely essential to the public good—hopefully these will have well thought-out approaches to maintaining your protection at work, and to maintaining PQ for you and your family.

In some situations the situation may involve the necessity of giving up your job if your place of work does not understand the issues as you do. However, entering into early discussions with your colleagues, learning your rights and benefits, and discussing your company's plan for business continuity during the Pandemic, will contribute to an easier transition time for you and your place of work. You may be able to work out a financial plan that is satisfactory to both you and the business. The best strategy is to clearly state your intentions early, and to prepare others with whom you associate. Forced withdrawal in the midst of the Pandemic will likely be a chaotic event. Regardless of what you and your family choose to do, consider all of your options at an early pre-pandemic time. Preparation is always far more effective than trying to respond after the fact.

CHAPTER FOUR:
ISOLATION

Once the sentinel event has signaled your retreat into Preventive Quarantine, you can expect to be in physical isolation for a significant period of time. There are different variables and expectations for different groups that make it difficult to give exact time frames. If the Pandemic races through the population and there appears to be less worry of rebound infections, three or four months might be a reasonable time frame. This time frame would have more risk than eight to twelve months would have, when one could be more certain that the virus had "run its course". These are estimates. Remember that the PQ concept is the best method for non-infection, and expect quarantine to last a long time. It should be your safest choice.

The Pandemic will be considered a national disaster. Depending on the virulence and deadliness of the mutated form of the virus, the adjectives appropriate to describe the severity of the disaster will vary. Lessons learned from Hurricane Katrina would project a time of desperation and despair that could have far-ranging consequences, during both this isolation time and beyond. In remembering Katrina, and attempting to draw conclusions about the likely course of a pandemic, it's important to realize that New Orleans had other places to potentially help or escape to. With the Pandemic, there will be no other sources of help, because all areas of the country, and of the world, will be caught up in the disaster. Catalyzed by inadequate and slow response of our disaster agencies and government, despairing people may turn to looting and violence. Although the isolation time on a well-prepared homestead and PQ community could be a pleasant experience, the overall "mood" of the country will likely be quite different. One must anticipate the influence of the country's mood on the mood of the PQ participants. It will be a significant factor for the leader(s) to deal with.

A. Leadership

During the pre-planning and isolation phases, an elected or consensus leader is needed to help guide the group through the trials and tribulations that are to be expected with such a dramatic endeavor. Excellent communication skills (especially listening skills) and the ability to make a clear decision and act upon it, will keep the leader in a respected position. The leader must be respected by the entire group, so that everyone will follow his/her decisions. Decisions should be made democratically, with the leader having the final say. This same approach is used on an expedition. Sometimes everyone agrees, and sometimes tough decisions must be made by the leader without everyone's easy agreement.

Members of the Preventive Quarantine must realize that this is not life as usual, but life that is carefully directed to prevent infection. The leader should have the most overall knowledge and understanding of this basic issue, in order to guide the group to a functional and healthy survival.

The leader will stay appraised of communications with the "outside world," and will hold regular meetings within the cell group and the quarantine community. If there are several families in a PQ community, the leaders from each unit will meet regularly.

The food and expendable supplies inventory lists will be kept by the leader, who may make decisive and effective adjustments to diet, water use, forays from the homestead, or any other significant issues affecting the group. It is the leader's duty and solemn obligation to make certain everyone understands the evolving overall picture nationally, regionally, and locally, as well as events in the PQ. The leader will call meetings or councils to discuss any particularly difficult issue.

B. Rules

Preventive quarantine group goals and objectives need to be established and agreed upon in the pre-quarantine period. Rules need to be clear, concise, and understandable. The consequences of breaking the rules must be equally clear. Everyone must understand that these consequences are impersonal and must understand the basics of risk stratification. Undoubtedly, important new decisions that have not been discussed may need to be made. In these situations, everyone needs to discuss the formation of any new rules, with the leader having the final say. Situations that could arise, such as pilfering of inventory supplies, need to be addressed. Solutions should relate more to prevention of the problem than to punishment. In other words, food and expendable supplies should be under lock and key, with the key held only by the leader. When rules are broken, pre-discussed consequences that fit the "crime" will not make the leader appear too strict or too lenient. Again, these are impersonal structures that are put in place for the safety and benefit of the group, not any individual.

Whatever the cause, there needs to be general agreement on handling death. For instance, an elderly quarantine member may die from a heart attack. Since funeral homes and morgues may be overwhelmed, plans regarding death need to be pre-addressed by clear rules. I specifically mention this, because death of any member of the quarantine will bring forth emphatic, emotional responses which may not be tempered by a leader's "uncaring" directives. Early discussion will reduce problems and increase compassionate understanding, should such an unfortunate event occur. Expeditions make similar preparations for similar reasons.

C. Specific Precautions

The prime directive of Preventive Quarantine is to avoid exposure to the pandemic flu virus as it spreads. Obviously, the virus is contagious and can be picked up from anyone who is sick with it. Since the first few days of the disease are often a-symptomatic, you can catch the virus from someone who has it, even though they may show no signs of the disease—no coughing, sneezing or runny nose. For these reasons, eliminating physical contact with people outside the quarantine is the essential rule. In addition, the virus is known to be able to stay alive and be contagious on semi-moist or even dry surfaces for several days, so it is possible to catch it from clothing, tools, vehicles, pets, furniture or buildings if they have been in close proximity with carriers of the virus.

This means that no one in the quarantine can have any physical contact with or be in close physical proximity with anyone from outside the quarantine once it has started. In addition, any physical contact with things from virus-rich zones must be carefully controlled, and the hands and clothing of the person venturing into the area disinfected.

Of course, physical contact means just that—there is no need to stay out of communication with the outside world during your quarantine time; and phone, TV, radio and Internet will be valuable tools so long as they stay in service.

Once quarantine is established, any person entering the quarantine needs to be isolated in a trailer or tent for seven to ten days before entering the main homestead area or physically interacting with others. This trailer or tent needs to be equipped with sufficient food and water supplies for the duration of that time frame, or safe means of delivering supplies need to be available. If a member leaving the quarantine area inadvertently comes in significant contact with others during a foray; then, upon returning to quarantine, they will need to be isolated for the same seven-to-ten-day timeframe. If quarantine rules are followed, participants should have no worry of getting the Pandemic Influenza.

Inside the quarantine, sharing spoons, water glasses, or other means of spreading communicable disease should be minimized by participants as a general practice, but the most significant concerns are directed toward the outside, viral-rich environments beyond the PQ.

All mail entering the homestead needs to be handled with gloves, or possibly sprayed with disinfectant. If entering the area in a "significant fashion," vehicles may need to be sprayed with a 9:1 solution of water and bleach. Neighborhood pets must be kept from entry, because their fur may carry the virus if they were exposed to sick individuals. No one is to pet stray animals. Hopefully, strays will find their way back home, or run the risk of being shot.

If it becomes necessary for a quarantine participant to foray into a viral-rich environment, Tamiflu could be given prophylactically to this person. If possible, a supply of Tamiflu should be obtained from your physician in the pre-quarantine period. No one is certain if Tamiflu will be effective, but it may reduce the severity of an infection. Use of gloves, masks, gowns, hair covers, shoe covers and goggles must become second nature when operating in any area that may have the virus. Barrier kits for forays (or any other encounters with potential carriers of the germ) should be portable and easily available to every participant.

Do not use any bleach with additives to disinfect drinking water. Only pure bleach is used for disinfecting water. Keep in mind that keeping water at a boil for three to five minutes is also an effective method for disinfection. Washing possibly-contaminated clothes with color-safe bleach (not the type for disinfection or water purification) will kill viruses.

Another important issue during quarantine is accident prevention. Respect for chainsaws, axes, knives, and other potentially dangerous tools or instruments needs to be emphasized. Prevention must rule, because there may be nowhere to get emergency medical treatment. Local emergency departments will be extremely viral-rich areas, and may do more harm in the long run.

Precautions must be emphasized in educating young quarantine participants. Children need to be taught proper techniques to prevent communicability of germs, especially mouth germs (including ways to cough, sneeze, hand wash, etc.). They also need to know how to protect themselves from others. Appropriate use of hand disinfectant cannot be emphasized enough; for adults, as well. These principles will hold them in good stead throughout their lives.

D. Living Strategies

In some ways, Preventive Quarantine could be likened to the experience of Anne Frank and her family. With due respect to the differences, both situations have a dangerous enemy outside the door. Undoubtedly, there was more day-to-day dread in the Frank's situation, especially with the "wailing" of those unforgettable sirens. However, Anne and her family were able to survive in a confined space for a considerable length of time before being captured. The Franks were able to deal with confinement, because they knew the consequences. We must also know our pandemic enemy, and the consequences of exposure.

While isolation from physical contact with others outside the cell group is the essential directive of PQ, one of the major strategies for making this isolation tolerable is to minimize time spent indoors. This is much easier to do in the country than in an urban environment. Hunting, fishing, and hiking can all be done without social contact. Having non-motorized vehicles available (or stashed amounts of fuel designated for short getaways) will be helpful.

As long as energy sources remain, electricity and fuel can be used. If and when those resources are not available, backup systems, such as "the way Grandma use to do it," will be necessary. Every main functional system needs to have a backup system, especially when the weather turns cold.

Besides backup systems, conserving expendable resources will be necessary. This can be summarized in the formula:

$$(1/2\ F) + (1/2\ P) + (2xT) = C.$$

This formula indicates that by eating one-half of the food (F) one normally would eat, using one-half of the amount of a product (P) that would regularly be used for any particular task, and taking twice as much time (T) between energy-consuming activities (such as washing clothes or showering) you can significantly conserve (C) your resources. Eating fewer calories than we normally consume is a healthier lifestyle. Cooking so there are no leftovers is a good habit. Much of this approach could also be adapted for healthier living outside of quarantine.

If automobiles can be used for activities, concentrating on efficient gas mileage will be critical. Gasoline may not be available, because of the inability to re-supply. Bicycles may rule the day. Reducing electrical use will also help preserve power for other families in your region. Demands on your heating systems can be reduced by lowering thermostats and dressing more warmly inside. Closing down infrequently-used rooms may allow the key rooms to be kept as warm as needed.

If at all possible, having personal space for everyone, even a tiny area, will be important for mental well-being.

If there are children in the quarantine, home schooling should be done. A pre-quarantine lesson plan will pay off at the time of PQ. Preparing children for the Pandemic is a very important task that cannot be neglected. Nor can any shortcuts be taken. Attention to understanding, in a child's way, the process that is unfolding, will modify anxiety later. Remember that love, attention, and constant reassurance are always good strategies. With children, as with adults, seeing this as an adventurous and challenging expedition can be a valuable mental and emotional strategy.

Duties around the homestead should be well-defined, and divided among all able participants. Regular schedules can be kept, which is comforting to children. There should be time for work and time for pleasure—probably in as equal amounts as possible. Accomplish many of the things you always wanted with your PQ time: read books, watch videos, garden, organize your family photographs and scrapbooks, indulge your hobbies, play family games, hunt, fish, hike, participate in home games and in preventive community activities. Activities with other quarantine families will help reduce stress and will help knit a more satisfying social fabric. Music fests, book clubs, dinners, movies, and magic shows—with creative minds, the possibilities are endless.

Siesta is now possible. (You've always wanted to try this anyway.)

To break the monotony for children, "surprises" should have been packaged in the pre-quarantine time and then disbursed in some regular fashion during the quarantine. Besides material surprises, new games, art work, activities, new almost anything can break the monotony. If children are part of your quarantine group, then look to them for imaginative ways to pass the time!

The leader will set regular homestead meetings. Leaders will update everyone on inventory lists, community activities, and news from the outside world.

Realizing that communication with the outside world could be very disturbing, you might want to have the leader make this contact and report to the group at regular intervals. More realistically, though, everyone has curiosity and is capable of tuning in the radio or TV. Perhaps discussions about the state of both the outside and the inside world can be conducted over meals, so that fears are addressed in the open.

Hygiene needs are crucial. The challenge will be when water is not easily available. A personal "feel good" attitude needs to be maintained for all, perhaps especially for the females. Extra cosmetics, etc., may seem extravagant, but the self-esteem they support can be worth the attention and stockpiling. Cleansing wipes with Aloe and non-sensitizing chemical additives can reduce hygienic water needs immensely. If water becomes scarce, and wet wipes run low, a simple sauna could be constructed for hygiene purposes. A water rinse is helpful, and if done just once a week it may be water-conserving. Water for hygiene purposes may be collected from rain or other sources.

Birth control must be practiced by those who are of childbearing age. The quarantine could last for nine or more months, and one does not want pregnancy complications during this time. Catholic participants, or other specific religious interests, may need special considerations brought into the homestead. Holy water availability may be necessary. For many, spiritual needs have obvious priorities.

If one planned wisely for special activities, designated cans of gasoline could be set aside for special trips to a distant fun spot. Travel forays from the base need to be viral protected. No new human contacts may be made. Adequate disinfectant and personal barrier protection equipment, such as gloves, masks, goggles, gowns, shoe covers, etc., need to be immediately available to each traveler. Most importantly, common sense needs to govern.

In many ways, living strategies for PQ can be very much like "old times," when self-sufficiency was the way of life. Preventive quarantine gives us the opportunity to experience the skills and processes that may have to become the norm, due to societal changes with the advent of fossil fuel depletion, global warming, or a variety of natural catastrophes. We have lost many of these skills and the stamina to engage them. The Pandemic may be the first domino on a path back to necessary self-sufficient lifestyles.

E. Forays

Forays from Preventive Quarantine may be necessary for any number of reasons. Most of the forays will probably be for fun, food or fuel. Food forays include the natural variety, such as fishing, hunting, or gathering berries. Fun activities could include hiking, canoeing, or short trips that don't expose participants to risk. Some forays may be for gasoline, and in such a situation, wearing gloves and disinfecting any touch spots would be absolutely necessary. One can always leave cash at the gasoline pump, so that one is not directly exposed to others. There is no risk involved in the outdoor environments where clean air, clean forests, and clean lakes abound. If there is an unintended encounter with people, a mask should be readily available, and common sense the order of the day. The type of mask that is most recommended is the 3M N95 mask. This mask probably gives more viral protection than a gauze mask or a typical surgical mask. If you are unable to get good masks, avoid situations where they may be needed. If absolutely necessary, improvise as best you can to provide some protection—two surgical masks can be worn at once, for instance, and fixed to the face at the edges with non-sensitizing tape.

Visits between PQ community families require no specific protection. As long as everyone is following the same rules, there should be no significant viral exposure, and therefore no significant protection needed. You will of course need great confidence in the integrity of the other units.

F. Communications

Communication is a vital part of successful Preventive Quarantine. This includes communication between the leader and the group, and between the leaders of the individual families in the PQ community. Leaders will need accurate and informative communication with the outside environment regarding the progress of the Pandemic and whether sentinel events are getting close, so that the quarantine can be ended. Rumors will abound. Good information sources are absolutely necessary.

Walkie-talkie communication with the base homestead may be important during hunting or fishing forays. Cellular telephone communication may be unavailable, as witnessed earlier with the Katrina disaster. Satellite telephones, although expensive, would be one of the last communications to be lost, but they are not practical for every homestead family. Regular telephone lines may or may not continue operating. A dependable communication medium for reaching outside the quarantine may be Ham radio, but, like satellite telephones, this is not a likely solution for most homesteads.

Battery-powered portable radios may be the mainstay of outside communications at times. If so, you may be able to use solar-powered rechargers to keep batteries going.

If the Pandemic reaches the high morbidity-mortality rate that is possible, communication with the outside world environment could be quite depressing. Feelings of sadness, loss, grief, frustration and fear need to be shared.

There is no guarantee that communication will lift everyone's spirits, but it generally helps enormously.

On the other side of the coin, the PQ can give a family an opportunity to reduce communication with the outside world for significant periods of time. This may allow peace and serenity to be more easily achieved. In today's hectic world, who has not sometimes yearned for a simpler, more peaceful time?

Contact with a medical facility could be important in several ways. For one, vaccination against the Pandemic virus could become available, once the strain is isolated and adequate supplies produced, although you won't be able to count on this. If the vaccine is available, a trip to the vaccination center would be enormously helpful and could signal the end of your quarantine. A vaccinated individual would posses immunity to the pandemic virus just like any surviving pandemic influenza victim would already have. Another reason for contact with a medical facility would be inquiring how to use medicines provided in your prescription medical kit you may have received from your physician, or for other medical advice. Telephone guidance could be easily accomplished, if personnel are available and communications systems are working. We do it for CPR now, why not regular medical advice on urgent or emergency parameters?

G. Defense

The concept of defending the isolated homestead has always been a part of the general "survivalist" culture. The reality of this situation is difficult to predict accurately. With Hurricane Katrina, we know that rescue and medical helpers were fired upon from sniper positions, so much so that armed escorts were needed to accompany rescue missions. The reason for this is difficult to understand. Severe catastrophic situations with slow or impossible rescue efforts cause people to change moods and thinking, and to act quite irrationally.

It is not difficult to envision a scenario where the majority of our society is placed under restrictions of food and water, causing some elements to act in irrational fashion. This could be very locale specific. Based on past experience, it would be more likely in urban settings than in rural ones. In rural settings, (untrue) signs at the gate that state,

"IN SEVERE QUARANTINE WITH INFLUENZA"

may be deterrent enough, although they won't necessarily stop people who are desparate for food and supplies. In urban settings, keeping a low profile and being ready for anything may be sensible.

It would certainly be advantageous for any particular homestead not to advertise their resources. It is the American way to have guns and ammunition and, whether these are used strictly for hunting game for food or for defending your homestead, there is no way to predict accurately the need for either.

The more likely problem of "invasion" of your homestead and private quarantine may be from friends and family who haven't prepared for Preventive Quarantine, and who did not heed earlier warnings. These situations will not require guns, but you may need to refuse them if you don't have the supplies or space. If you are able to take them in, then they will need to stay in the transitional area for seven to ten days, as described above. There is no easy way to tell a relative or a friend that they are not able to enter the homestead due to short supplies, fear of contamination, or not enough space. A realistic assessment of the consequences of your decision will help you live with the decision once it's made.

H. Fire/Police/Ambulance/Medical Emergencies

At the height of the Pandemic Fire, Police and Ambulance personnel will almost certainly be overwhelmed and unavailable. These courageous public servants, if they have remained in the workforce during the early stages of the Pandemic, will probably have fallen victim to the virus, despite their self-protection equipment. Or, they will be caring for family members who have fallen victim to the influenza. The pandemic will also lead to an increase in other types of emergencies, due to interruption of services and social disruption, and other emergencies will also continue to happen. Even if emergency personnel and facilities are available, the hospitals and emergency rooms will be viral-rich environments. More than ever, during the Pandemic, you must do everything in your power to prevent injuries, fires, physical violence and other emergencies from occurring in the first place. We have become so accustomed to having a sophisticated safety net in place around us, that special attention must be paid to the fact that it may not be there for large periods of time during the Pandemic.

For medical problems, it would certainly be helpful to have a nurse, paramedic, EMT (emergency medical technician), or physician in your community group. Lacking such people, information can be obtained from a good medical book, from the Internet, or from calls to appropriate medical resources. Having everyone's medicine available and having a good medical kit will be important. The leader needs to have a complete medical history on each participant with allergies, obtained hopefully in the preparation phase.

Many medical or traumatic emergencies can be handled in the home environment with the appropriate equipment, medicines, and ability to talk with experts by telephone. Making a decision to break quarantine in order to obtain help elsewhere will be difficult indeed. With sufficient planning, many health care facilities may have set up medical "facilities" away from hospitals or clinics. The leader of the Preventive Quarantine needs to stay in contact with such developments, because these facilities may have a lower risk of infection associated with them. If a patient receives help outside of quarantine and returns, they need to remain in the trailer quarantined just outside the main core for seven to ten days. This same would be true of the driver if they are a member of the PQ community.

What can be done regarding fire issues? Certainly, having fire extinguishers for the three types of fires (A, B, C[1]), is important. Fire prevention is critically important. Having community members who can gather together and help each other in case of fire (or any other emergency) gives an additional measure of protection. Wood burning and some other alternative methods of heat significantly increase the risk of fire. Rarely-used chimneys may ignite from newly hot fires. Knowing how to extinguish chimney fires may save your home from destruction.

Your physical security from outside violence will also be in your own hands. The issues here will be dependent on your area and the degree of devastation in the outside community. The closely-knit quarantine members can act as a "Crime Watch" community.

There should be places within the homestead or PQ community to retreat in case of natural disasters, such as a tornado. Well-thought-out plans allow for less potential for contamination during a "rush" to shelter. A NOAA portable weather radio with alert signals can be a big help.

In the later stages of your PQ, a Pandemic vaccine may have been completed. Transport, then, to a vaccination clinic could be an important venture. By the time a vaccine is developed, viral exposure may also be at a minimum since the Pandemic may have begun to exhaust itself. Whether this is actually true or not, of course, will be a matter for expert opinion. You will need to have excellent sources of outside information in order to track the progress of the

---

1 See Appendices for types of fires.

Pandemic and to judge the level of risk. As mentioned above, the 1918 Pandemic came in separate waves, with the second wave far more deadly than the first.

CHAPTER FIVE:
AFTERMATH

At some point, this infectious catastrophe will end. The Pandemic Influenza will burn itself out because it will eventually have difficulty finding sufficient hosts to infect, and will go into the "used virus gene pool." One of the issues with isolation is that you need to have a sentinel event to exit from the Preventive Quarantine. In terms of exposure to the virus this is a relative risk situation. The risk of catching the pandemic flu will increase from the time that the virus first enters your area and will then eventually decrease as it runs out of new people to infect. During this period, it is difficult to assess with accuracy what the risk of infection will be as the virus runs its course. If one exits the PQ after only two to four months, there is theoretically a high relative risk of infection and possible death. If one waits eight to twelve months the risk should be much lower (although this is dependent upon the number of waves in which the pandemic occurs).

It is my assumption from looking at previous epidemics that if you plan for one entire year of PQ it would be more than necessary. Half that time may be a more reasonable compromise under most circumstances.

If the pandemic comes in three waves, as the 1918 Pandemic did, then you would need to be in isolation for more than twelve months to be completely safe. It is possible, during this period, that one could make forays between waves with relatively less exposure. If one plans and stocks for a year and it then turns out that the quarantine can be foreshortened, so much the better. If it needs to be extended in order to cover another wave then perhaps this could be done through carefully controlled forays, as the situation allows.

There are two keys to exiting your quarantine. The first is knowing with some accuracy when the disease has run its course. The second is the ability to obtain an effective vaccination for the pandemic virus. Both of these are relative, not absolute. Even when the pandemic is over and no new cases are being seen, there are still small amounts of the virus extant in the environment and it is possible for someone who has not previously been exposed to catch the pandemic flu. The combination of having the virus run its course and getting vaccinated will provide a high degree of possibility that you won't get the disease, or that if you do catch it, the illness will be much less severe.

The World Health Organization (WHO) and Centers for Disease Control (CDC) should be able to give us the information we need for making the exiting decision. In addition to knowing from the WHO and CDC whether the pandemic has run its course, it will be important to know if a vaccine has become available for the pandemic strain. If so, then the participants should be vaccinated as soon as feasible so they can gain immunity to the virus.

The exiting of participants in each of the families or groups in the PQ community needs to be coordinated. This is why communication among the leaders of the different homesteads, homes or apartments is important. Each participating unit may choose to have a different exiting time. One unit may think a six-month quarantine is appropriate for them while others may want to go longer. Upon termination of the isolation period, healthy participants from the PQ can now volunteer for the necessary rebuilding and restructuring of society during the aftermath.

Society, having benefited from the reduced load on healthcare systems that PQ participants produced, can now benefit from the presence of a number of people that have stayed healthy. Many of those in the larger population could still be suffering from the physical effects of the illness as well as mentally, emotionally and spiritually from the deaths of friends and loved ones. You, also, will have friends, acquaintances and possibly family members that were not in quarantine with you who may have suffered from the illness or even died from it.

In the aftermath, there may continue to be significant financial disruption, as well as considerable financial opportunity. Your specific situation will be greatly impacted by your skill sets, your ability to adapt to the present circumstances, and by the amount of cash and debt you have.

Your immediate financial disruption can be significantly reduced by having, as far as possible, a considerable amount of liquid assets at your immediate disposal. Recall the lessons learned during the Great Depression. Money left in financial institutions was lost (although this is much less likely today).

The stock market may suffer or improve, or may vary widely by industry. How your pension profit sharing plan or social security and other similar vehicles will fare depends on many things. Hopefully the government, banks and lenders will work out a plan such that payments on mortgages and other debts can be suspended without penalty (while perhaps continuing to accrue interest), so that we don't see widespread default on loans.

There may be no jobs available, or there may be many job opportunities. To some degree, the aftermath time may resemble the depression of the 1930s. It may be advantageous to continue the small community group that functioned so well during the quarantine time. I suspect many people will have had a positive experience. Some may not want to re-enter the social fabric again. Individual responses to the aftermath will be unique to each individual and family.

CHAPTER SIX:
PREVENTIVE QUARANTINE—YES OR NO

The likelihood of participation in any prevention scheme that involves a fair amount of investment, preparation, work and sacrifice is typically low. Most of us change only with actual catastrophe or crisis rather than in preparation for a crisis—even if the likelihood of the crisis occurring is quite high. However, there are a number of reasons to think differently about Preventive Quarantine.

The first and most obvious reason is that it could save your life, or the lives of your loved ones. You may want to undertake the practice for this reason, even if there were no other.

A second reason is more altruistic. If a significant percentage of us were to employ an appropriate PQ it could slow the progression of the Pandemic virus by eliminating some of the fuel from the advancing "fire". Because isolation reduces the opportunity to infect hosts, it could reduce the phenomenon known as "passage" in viral infections. "Passage" is likely responsible for an increased severity in the second wave of a pandemic because the virus gains virulence as it rapidly infects more and more hosts. Slowing this rapid process would provide additional time for things such as vaccine development or better delivery of essential services. It is a method, like closing schools, that can flatten the peak incidence of cases over time. Methods like these are recommended by the World Health Organization, and others, when there are insufficient pharmaceutical treatments available for control.

Reducing the load on over-burdened health care and supply systems is the third reason to consider PQ. The more people that are able to successfully avoid exposure to the virus, the fewer there are that will need care. In addition, getting supplies before-hand reduces the pressure on the stores and delivery systems when the Pandemic hits.

Fourthly, although the PQ practice keeps you from having physical contact with those outside your quarantine group, it doesn't prevent you from being in active communication via the Internet, phone, radio or mail. You might be able to continue some aspects of your previous work, take on some other type of "virtual" work, or contribute in certain ways to the efforts to deal with the pandemic. There are many possibilities that haven't been discussed here.

This book is written for you and your family. It was not written to change national or state policies. Hopefully it will help make you more knowledgeable and will encourage you to make early planning a priority. The PQ approach may be the only way we know to assure surviving a pandemic without illness and death. We assume that this is important to you. Hopefully this book will give you the information and motivation you need to make good decisions.

Plan ahead with your job. Make your priorities clear at an early stage of discussion with your place of employment. You may be better off in terms of job security and financial stability after the pandemic. Involuntarily leaving your job when you or your co-workers become ill only increases the probability of serious consequences for you. It also increases chaos in the work environment. Your discussions and planning ahead of time may encourage your workplace to begin serious "business continuity planning" as the International Monetary Fund has been urging all businesses to do in preparing for the Pandemic.

On emerging from quarantine you are a more healthy, capable worker ready to pitch in and contribute to your job and society.

There are certainly advantages of being exposed to common sense sustainable living. The simplicity and isolation may appeal to some and be maddening for others but for many individuals there seems to be a quest for a "simpler life." I suspect some of those in PQ will desire to continue in the sustainable style.

There may be some disadvantages to the PQ approach, as well. One is the removal of skilled volunteers and help during the onslaught of the pandemic. It is likely that those successfully executing PQ may be among those that are more skilled and have more resources. It is my opinion that PQ can reduce the load on the care system more than it will reduce the abilities of the system to provide care. Those deemed as absolutely essential to keep the fabric of society together will have to take a close and realistic look at strategies that could encompass both viral protection at work and family safety in PQ, with sound barrier protection for traveling in between. They may even have to make a difficult value decision between staying with and protecting their family and staying with their job.

There are other implications with this approach. Money is needed to get the necessary supplies. Time and work are needed to plan and prepare. Many people simply cannot give that amount of time or cash to such an effort. Leaving your job two weeks earlier than necessary (when the pandemic forces your withdrawal) might make little difference but it could make a considerable financial difference. You must consider these scenarios ahead of time. Not having the income from your employment will certainly be a burden but, of course, the burden may be present anyway for those forced from their job or source of income by the repercussions of the pandemic. My approach is to prepare for it by assessing the risks to your financial well-being and weighing these against the other risks as you see them—and making some decisions.

Setting money aside now could lighten the burden. Reasonable amounts set aside each month before it hits could accumulate to a substantial sum if the pandemic holds off for one to two years. Getting out of debt as much as you can now is a strong recommendation.

Good professional financial advice is necessary. However, seek advice from someone who ideally understands all the aspects of the pandemic.

CHAPTER SEVEN:
CONCLUSIONS

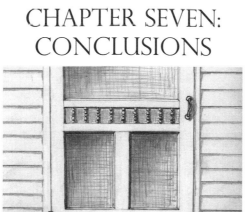

The only thing that matches the incredible concept of six-to-twelve months in a Preventive Quarantine is catching a glimpse of the equally incredible disruption and disaster likely from a Pandemic Influenza.

Look at the pictures of the 1918 Influenza Pandemic, listen to the stories, read the descriptions of pandemic influenza. Now imagine something similar but more devastating. If you can relate to the imagery, you will find yourself able to entertain the concept of PQ. However, if this book simply acts as a wake up call making you more aware of the real potential for a pandemic, it will have served a useful purpose.

There are many recent examples of the failure of our larger social systems to effectively provide for those in catastrophic distress. It is not a stretch to assume that the best helping hand is at the end of our own arm. In the broadest context, this book is about more than the Pandemic Influenza. It presents us with one of our "last opportunities" to approach an answer to the more complicated problems of the Earth. The aftermath could be a time when people say, "Hmm, PQ wasn't so bad. As a matter of fact, I enjoyed the peace and serenity, and the relative good health. Perhaps if I could combine my ingenuity and sustainable skills, along with a few creative creature comforts here and there, this is how I would like to live. I now know that I can take care of myself and my family. I have a small community around me that functions well together. I believe I will give it a try..."

The survivors within urban settings may have a different response. Rural homesteads may see the vision more clearly. Our society has been seduced into believing that our technology can solve everything and that democracy around the world will solve all our international problems. Most of us do not believe that depletion of fossil fuels is a disaster awaiting us soon. Perhaps the pandemic can awaken us to human resourcefulness and allow us to see through the pipe dream of our materialistic and energy expensive desires. We will need a new type of "heart" to meet the more complex problems ahead. We certainly cannot eat our computers. We cannot digest our investments nor really survive without good food, good water, good air and with knowledge of the skills needed to develop, manage and sustain these necessities.

The twentieth century was an incredible time of booming material development. We pushed back many frontiers, typically at the expense of our natural resources. We walked on the moon, spanned the globe, and "conquered disease." But we were caught up in the destructive vision of unbounded progress based on technology. Do we have time to become more realistic? No one knows. I do know that there are a few things I can do. I know that sustainable living skills are well suited to the challenges presented by the Pandemic.

I have had an opportunity to talk to some of my relatives who lived through the Great Depression in the 1930s. They do not have the complacency that this generation has. We seem to be numbed by mass media hypnosis and apathy derived from the tremendous amount of spin put on every bit of information we receive. Our economists stick to ever-expanding "growth" economics despite the reality of steadily depleted resources and a finite planet. We hardly consider the next generation, let alone the seventh generation[1], in making our decisions. How the world will emerge from the pandemic will be anyone's guess. It could be the first of a series of domino-disasters that collectively sets our civilization back.

In 1967 the Surgeon General of the United States, Williams Stuart, declared "it is time to close the book on infectious disease." The pandemic will show us how naive this statement was. Let us work so that infectious disease doesn't "close the book" on us!

---

1 *The Iroquois, who developed a democratic form of governance upon which our own was partially modeled, said that we must consider the implications of our decisions over "seven generations".*

SKIP HOFSTRAND MD is a board certified Emergency Physician currently working full time. He also has a PhD in Anatomy with a minor in Zoology and Chemistry from the University of Minnesota. He has been a medical consultant to 6 major Arctic and Antarctic expeditions and now lives rurally in Northern Minnesota. He has long been an on-again, off-again resident of Ely, MN—his spiritual retreat destination. He has many scientific publications and has written the chapter on Accidental Hypothermia and Frostbite in the leading Pediatric Emergency textbook in the country. He was recently appointed Medical Director of the Summit Project, a Duluth, grassroots, community based, project designed to help an urban neighborhood within the City of Duluth meet the Pandemic Influenza safely.

SUE SEME is a rural housewife considered by her husband and friends to be an expert in sustainable country living. She is also a professional artist and illustrator and her illustrations grace this book. Sue also lives rurally in Northern, Minnesota. She is co-director of Images of the Mind, an art business and studio run from her homestead.

APPENDICES

I. Scientific Facts that should make you concerned About the Upcoming Pandemic Influenza   I-5

II. Reasons We might be using to ignore the Upcoming Pandemic II-9

III. The Eight Principles of Preventive Quarantine   III-11

IV. Preplanning and Supply Acquisition For preventive Quarantine IV-15

    A. Questions to ask yourself when considering a PQ/PQC.   IV-15

    B. Steps to begin a PQ—either rural or urban.   IV-16

    C. Key features of a PQ.   IV-19

    D. Possible PQ-entry sentinel events.   IV-37

    E. Food and water.   IV-38

    F. Expendable supply list (not including food/water/fuel).   IV-60

    G. Essential equipment list.   IV-62

    II. Medical lists.   IV-66

    I. "Gosh, Darn, Heck!!" scramble list.   IV-79

    J. Grab list for a PQ participant who must leave fast and come a distance to the PQ.   IV-81

V. PQ social isolation period   V-83

    A. General rules for a PQ.   V-83

    B. General rules for a PQ Community.   V-84

    C. How to deal with potential PIV exposures or actual exposures.   V-85

    D. Medical Strategies.   V-88

    E. Sentinel event examples for PQ exit.   V-94

VI. References   VI-95

    A. General books.   VI-95

    B. Catalogues   VI-96

    C. Key articles.   VI-96

    D. Official sources of information.   VI-97

    E. Web sites to know.   VI-97

    F. Stores selling bulk foods.   VI-98

    G. Financial resources.   VI-98

There have been a number of articles and books on the Pandemic Influenza. However, few, if any, give detailed helpful how-to information in an easy, step-by-step format, especially preparing for, living through, and finally emerging from the Pandemic.

Many of us have lived through the less severe Pandemics of 1957 and 1968, but likely do not remember them in any special way. Very few of us can remember the 1918 Pandemic. If the 1918 Pandemic were in our personal memory, we would probably be acting quite differently now.

This appendix will give you step-by-step directions, supply lists, and other useful information about the Preventive Quarantine approach to the upcoming Pandemic. Under each section, where relevant, there will be discussion or directions for both urban and rural PQs.

It is to be noted that urban PQ planning, using the same principles as rural PQ planning, will require a certain degree of creativity. Barrier device use will need to be more extensive in the urban environment, since there are may more real or potentially viral-rich contamination sources always close at hand. Barrier device use and associated strategies need to become second nature to the urban resident, almost reflexive.

Regardless of urban or rural designation, if there are adequate food and water supplies, adequate emergency systems, adequate power grids, and undisturbed communication systems, it could almost be life as usual, except for the social isolation. However, if the devastation becomes immense, with great disruptions, then extensive preplanning and preparation will make all the difference.

The Preventive Quarantine Community will work best if it remains small, 10-12 units or fewer. It can then typically maintain its ultimate barrier boundary more effectively.

I. SCIENTIFIC FACTS THAT SHOULD MAKE YOU CONCERNED ABOUT THE UPCOMING PANDEMIC INFLUENZA

A. The known Pandemics of this century: The Spanish Pandemic Influenza of 1918, the Asian Pandemic Influenza of 1957, and the Hong Kong Pandemic Influenza of 1968, were all bird influenza's that mutated to the human pandemic form. The Spanish Pandemic Influenza was an H1N1 type, the Asian Pandemic Influenza was an H2N2 type, and the Hong Kong Pandemic Influenza was an H3N2 type. The 1918 Pandemic was extremely severe, and the 1957 and 1968 Pandemics were much less severe. New virological studies at the United States Institute of Pathology, published in the Fall of 2005, has indicated that the present H5N1 influenza form that is rapidly spreading around the world, is mutating like the 1918 pre-Pandemic germ, and not like the 1957 or 1968 forms. With this discovery, the World Health Organization (WHO) and the Center for Disease Control (CDC) have dramatically increased their concerns for this upcoming Pandemic.

B. There have been many Pandemic Influenzas in the previous centuries, but the historical records are not complete enough to make specific statements about them. For instance, the Russian Pandemic Influenza of 1890 has not been able to be typed like the others. The point is that Pandemic Influenzas are naturally recurring phenomenon. You can absolutely count on them happening, but you can't set your clock by them.

C. The world is now experiencing an H5N1 pandemic form in birds. This rapidly- advancing pandemic in poultry and certain migrating waterfowl significantly increases the "breeding ground" for the next mutation to human-to-human transmitted Pandemic

Influenza. The H5N1 form presently in birds has steadily spread since its first discovery in 1996. It is constantly mutating, as do all influenza forms, but present research finds it very close to the mutation that will allow effective human-to-human transmission.

D. Because they have handled or had close contact with sick birds, the occasional humans infected with the present H5N1 bird flu form have developed very serious infections. To-date, there are over 200 reported cases, with approximately one-half resulting in death. This means that the present H5N1 bird form is not easily transmitted to humans at this time, but that the lethality of those infected portends ominous consequences, if this H5N1 form becomes the upcoming Pandemic. There, of course, remains the slim chance that the next mutation could make the Pandemic less severe, but the evidence at present points the other way.

E. If the upcoming Pandemic is anything like the 1918 Spanish Pandemic, it will cause catastrophic problems all over the world. The problems will not just relate to direct human suffering, but to elements of our global infrastructure. Given the rapid global travel and many other factors of our 21st Century life, the computer models show that the virus will travel around the world very quickly, once it begins. They indicate a time measured in weeks before it affects every corner of the globe. Not enough time for one to adequately prepare, once the announcement has been made.

F. Although there is a slim chance the H5N1 avian influenza will mutate into a less severe human Pandemic form, the scientific information points otherwise. Is it wise behavior to not prepare for something as potentially catastrophic as the 1918 Pandemic -- or worse? If you could accurately imagine the consequences of non-preparation, not only for yourself and your family, but for our country as a whole, you would have no trouble beginning immediate planning.

G. There are no medical or technological solutions to help intervene in any significant fashion. Belief in technological "fairy tales" will not help. Nor will belief that government can help in the immediate short run (in the long run, changing our vaccine development program can have some positive impact for future pandemics). From a medical point of view, and from a government rescue point of view, we are no better off in 2006 than we were in 1918.

H. The H5N1 virus is constantly mutating. It's seemingly doing everything possible to gain a foothold in humans. The bird flu roulette "gun chamber" has eight tiny genes. The mutation hammer is soon ready to connect. There is a way to prepare, however, and to greatly minimize the impact of the coming Pandemic—Plan Plan Plan, Prepare Prepare Prepare, Preventive Quarantine.

II. REASONS WE MIGHT BE USING TO IGNORE THE UPCOMING PANDEMIC

You may find yourself with one or more of the following reasons for not preparing seriously for the pandemic. If so, you might want to examine these thoughts and see if you're acting on the basis of your *best* current thinking.

A. Memories of past potential problems that did not materialize for one reason or another (example Y2K). "Is this just another of those?"

B. The belief that our technology will supply all the answers and rescue us.

C. The constant media bombardment of problems around the world, so the avian influenza news just gets lost to our immediate attention.

D. Our government will take care of the situation (despite the evidence from Hurricane Katrina).

E. It's easier to be reactive, rather than proactive, in dealing with problems. "Let it happen, and then I will deal with it."

F. The majority of our society has no actual personal memory of the 1918 Pandemic severity, nor of significant prolonged periods of devastation, such as the Great Depression, therefore we don't have any "gut feel" that it can happen.

G. A certain cultural apathy is prevalent, which has many faces, but has resulted in a strong inertia against accomplishing reasonable and common sense objectives.

H. The past Pandemics of 1957 and 1968 give us a "can't be so bad" sense.

I. I don't want to look like a kook reactionary; I just want to be cool... or at least appear cool.

J. I'm tired of all this talk about catastrophes. What can I really do anyway?

K. The apocalypse will come regardless of how we try to avoid it... and God will provide for us.

L. This is just a government and pharmaceutical company conspiracy to scare us into buying lots of Tamiflu.

III. THE EIGHT PRINCIPLES OF PREVENTIVE QUARANTINE

A. Preventive Quarantine is the ultimate "barrier device" by which you and your family can prevent infection by the Pandemic Influenza virus (PIV). No exposure....no infection is the mantra.

B. PQ is total *voluntary* social isolation by healthy individuals. PQ is different from the usual definition of quarantine, which involves isolation of already sick or exposed-to-germ individuals.

C. PQ employs a risk stratification process, i.e. the risk of infection is directly related to how early PQ is entered, and to the length of time within the PQ. Sentinel events mark entry and exit dates.

D. PQ can have a positive effect on the general public health, and on the general public good by these mechanisms.

1. Individuals participating in PQ will not get infected, and therefore, will not put additional strain on the health care system.

   a. No emergency department visits for Pandemic Influenza.

   b. No hospitalization stays for PI.

   c. No ventilators/critical medical equipment supplies use for PI.

2. Individuals involved in PQ will have shopped for their supplies before the mad rush begins, thereby leaving more on store shelves to be acquired by latecomers. Early stockpiling contributes to the economy before the economy feels the sudden impact of the PIV.

3. Individuals removed from the direct line of the PIV "fire" could slow progression of the virus and contribute to a reduction

in its early virulence, similar to removing the brush and small trees from the path of an early-stage forest fire. This slowing of the PIV passage through our human population would allow additional time for specific vaccine development, and could contribute to more effective essential services delivery. This phenomenon of "passage," as it is called, occurs when a microorganism of a known lethality begins its spread from animal to animal, and in the process of infecting more and more hosts in rapid-fire progression, gains virulence (infectivity) and lethality (deadliness). Passage allows the microorganism to spread more effectively and efficiently, and to become more dangerous. Slowing this progression (by removing the hosts) maximizes the time before the virus reaches its most destructive form. In 1918, the second wave of PIV that occurred on the heels of the first wave was more lethal and devastating than the first. The explanation to this lies partly in the viral "passage" phenomenon.

4. Individuals planning PQ require early discussion meetings, especially with their place of employment (and also with their schools, churches, and other significant organizations), such that appropriate and effective decision-making can be pre-planned regarding the timing of their social isolation. This will allow a more effective business plan for employers, and hopefully contribute to a more survivable strategy for the business. Contrast this with employees rapidly disbursing when the PIV hits the community, and business attempting to cope with an unplanned environment void of workers. Work planned in advance might be accomplished from within the PQ. Other strategies need be planned for those employees involved in truly *essential* services. Perhaps the job site can be a foray site with precautions and rules strictly adhered to in order to prevent viral exposure. Planning ahead has to be a winning strategy, regardless.

5. Individuals emerging from their PQ should be healthy, without the health issues that surviving PIV victims might have. Remember, the PIV affects all systems of the body, and may leave, for example, one's heart, lungs, kidneys, or some combination of

such, in much worse condition than they were pre-PIV. Healthy individuals can more effectively help with the infrastructure needs of a devastated community. Healthy employees will be able to contribute more to their workplaces than those disabled by the PIV.

6. Individuals from PQ and the PQ Community may well act as models for healthy, sustainable living strategies during future crises or catastrophes, thereby contributing to the public good.

E. PQ is planning, planning, and more planning. The PQ is very similar to the expedition. An expedition's success is directly proportional to the degree of planning partaken, and it will be the same with your PQ. You can do it! Your life and your family's lives may depend upon it.

F. PQ, despite what thoughts you may have, can be done for long periods of time. It is not an impossible scenario, and it could be a pleasant experience, depending upon your degree of planning, and your ability to stockpile essential supplies. It can be accomplished in either a rural or urban environment, and will likely be creative and unique to each setting.

G. PQ isolation rules absolutely govern, and everyone involved in the PQ or in your Preventive Quarantine Community, must adhere to the rules established by your PQ and PQC. Rules may be somewhat different between PQs, due to different events signaling entry and exit times. PQs also need a designated leader, who can help the group make difficult decisions. Such a decision-maker needs to be informed, respected, and wise. Remember, the prime purpose of the PQ approach is to prevent exposure to the PIV. This will require discipline.

H. Although the concept of PQ and PQC, to some, may seem to be a withdrawal from contributing to the public's good, it is supported by individuals who are very knowledgeable about the spectrum of problems the Pandemic presents to everyone, everywhere. Each PQ leader is encouraged to get involved in larger community, region, state, and federal planning efforts. Upon exit from PQ, as well, there exists an equal obligation to help with the aftermath, whatever devastation has been wrought. Each PQ participant should feel a vital part of the process of the public's health, and the overall public good.

IV. PREPLANNING AND SUPPLY ACQUISITION FOR PREVENTIVE QUARANTINE

A. Questions to ask yourself when considering a PQ/PQC.

1. Do I understand what the upcoming Pandemic is, and what could happen to myself, my family, and my neighbors?

2. Do I understand how contagious and dangerous this virus could be?

3. Do I understand what Preventive Quarantine will actually mean for me, my family, and my neighbors?

4. Do I understand the difference between social isolation and social distancing?

5. Can I adhere to rules when absolutely necessary and lives are potentially at stake? Can I follow a respected leader?

6. Can I be helpful and creative in a PQ or a PQC?

7. Do I or my family have significant problems that would lead to more problems with a PQ or a PQC?

8. Can I put common sense and survivability ahead of emotion and past habits, if necessary?

9. Can I practice food, water, and supplies conservation if necessary?

10. Do I have family members who would not respect the rules or the leader?

B. Steps to begin a PQ—either rural or urban.

RURAL

__ 1. Understand all aspects of a pandemic and make a decision.

__2. Know what my community, hospital, schools, and workplace are doing to prepare.

__3. Interact with all of above (#2), and understand the potential implications of your social isolation (especially your job).

__4. Begin reducing debt, as able, and set aside cash for supplies and reserve.

__5. Decide how many participants will be in your PQ.

__6. Decide site for the PQ.

__7. Will there be participants that are saying "No" now, but will likely come later? (In any case, plan for them.)

__8. Meet with actual or potential participants in PQ, and review plans with them. Discuss rules to be followed.

__9. Determine total number to plan for (relates to factors such as space), so supply amounts and lists can be started.

__10. Set sentinel event for entry.

__11. With the money that is available, begin supply acquisition as per lists and directions in this book. (Acquire each week or month as money is available.)

__12. Creatively modify the chosen home/homestead, to meet future needs.

__13. Begin conversations and meetings with neighbors regarding their plans and interest in forming a PQC.

__14. Finalize the PQC, if able. Units need not be next door, but within walking or biking distance is best. Other means of travel could be used, if gasoline supply can be assured. Make certain everyone agrees with the rules.

__15. Continue supply acquisition.

__16. Continue saving money. Purchase extra prescription needs and other medical supplies.

__17. Anticipate and visit foray spots: gas stations, wilderness, fishing/hunting areas, berry patches and fruit trees.

__18. Have regular meetings with other PQC leaders.

URBAN

__1. Understand all aspects of a pandemic and make a decision.

__2. Know what my community, hospital, schools, and workplace are doing to prepare.

__3. Interact with all of above (#2), and understand the potential implications of your social isolation (especially your job).

__4. Begin reducing debt, as able, and setting aside cash for supplies and reserve.

__5. Decide how many participants will be in your PQ.

__6. Decide if you will stay in your urban setting or go with family/friends to a rural PQ. Since storage units could solve problems, choosing a rural setting may not be necessary.

__7. Will there be participants that are saying "No" now, but will likely come later? (In any case, plan for them.)

__8. Meet with actual or potential participants in PQ, and review plans with them. Discuss rules to be followed.

__9. Determine total number to plan for (relates to factors such as space), so supply amounts and lists can be started.

__10. Set sentinel event for entry.

__11. With the money that is available, begin supply acquisition as per lists and directions in this book. (Acquire each week or month as money is available.)

__12. Creatively modify the apartment or home, to meet future needs, especially as they relate to food storage/participants/ability to maintain social isolation in close proximity to others/food preparation back-up/water storage/etc.

__13. Begin conversations and meetings with neighbors regarding their plans and interest in forming a PQC.

__14. Finalize the PQC, if able. If it's an apartment complex, it would be advantageous if the entire complex or certain floors could belong to the same PQC plan. Be creative. Make certain everyone agrees with the rules.

__15. Continue supply acquisition. Acquire important potential helps, like a breadmaker.

__16. Continue saving money. Purchase extra prescription needs and other medical supplies.

__17. Anticipate and visit foray spots: gas stations, wilderness or similar, parks and recreation areas, food stores. (May designate special gas cans for this travel.) Can you have complete barrier protection in these places?

__18. Have regular meetings with other PQC leaders.

C. Key features of a PQ.

1. Energy and resource considerations.

   a. Heat

      i. Anticipate both heating and cooling strategies.

      ii. Do we have back-up systems? Are they portable?

      iii. Sufficient clothing and sleeping bags/blankets available?

      iv. Number of fans (a fan blowing across a pan of water that has a cloth hanging into the water can be a makeshift air conditioner).

      v. For safety issues, be careful about pushing the limits of any system; which could produce, for example, chimney fires, carbon monoxide, etc.

      vi. Adjust thermostats to a lower setting in winter; air conditioners to a higher setting during summer.

      vii. Strategize to prevent water pipes from freezing/bursting.

      viii. Outdoor fires for heat.

   b. Power considerations.

      i. Auxiliary systems, especially for water pump—generators (gas or propane) for intermittent use.

      ii. Auxiliary systems in urban areas could be more challenging. Consider solar systems for essentials, as affordable.

      iii. Propane conversion kits are available for gasoline powered generators.

      iv. Concentrate on using non-electrical, non-fuel backup approaches where possible. (Remember the old days when the best power source wore your shoes?)

v. Even though the time periods here seem long, the power shortages, if they happen at all, may not last the entire length of your PQ.

c. Water supply considerations.

i. *Water is the most critical of all supplies.* Without good water to drink, severe problems or death are not far behind. We can survive for long periods of time by drastically lowering food consumption, if necessary. Not so with water. We need a specific amount each day. PREPARE.

ii. Electrical back-up (generator) will be necessary to get water from your well if the electrical supply grid is down.

iii. I have gone into detail on ways to purify any water, if needed. This should allow you to extend your sources (see v. below).

iv. Store, store, store, especially if you're in an urban setting, but also if there is no back-up rurally. Each person will need 8 gallons of water per week for drinking and minimal sanitation.

v. Consider all sources that could be available; lakes/streams/etc., so long as you can purify the water you obtain from them.

vi. Rig a system to collect rain water.

d. Waste management considerations.

i. In general, don't flush every urination if water supply is restricted.

ii. In apartment settings, urine and feces can be collected in separate containers or strong plastic bags. Or use a camping porta-potty, with appropriate chemicals.

iii. Storage or disposal must be planned, perhaps buried later. No paper.

iv. Shallow holes with sand bottoms can be temporarily used outside. For natural decomposition, leave enough space at the top to fill with at least six inches of earth.

v. Beware of putting excessive chlorine into home septic systems—it can kill the beneficial micro-organisms needed to effectively treat the sewage.

vi. Organic garbage can be composted rurally, with other trash stored in bags. Certain urban sites may also be able to compost.

e. Lighting considerations.

i. Lighting is an important consideration for mental health.

ii. Candles and kerosene lanterns are not bright enough for reading, but are suitable for safety or task lighting.

iii. Aladdin kerosene lamps give great light, but can be difficult to manage, unless you are experienced.

iv. Battery operated flashlights and lamps are convenient.

v. Use light sparingly. Finish tasks during daylight hours. Radio can be listened to in the dark.

vi. There is a new lantern on the market by Survival Unlimited, called Petromax. It burns anything, including isopropyl alcohol (which means it can be burned indoors). It's very bright, and can also be used for cooking. If you have a "still" that produces alcohol, you will be able to produce your own fuel.

2. Storage/space considerations.

a. Food storage/useful life.

i. Cans or manufacturer foil-sealed canned goods. Keep from high temperatures.

ii. Dry packed or sealed boxed containers. Keep from moisture/light/high temperatures. Includes powdered milk, white flour, whole grains, rolled oats, legumes, pasta (that does not contain egg products), dehydrated fruit/vegetables (apples/bananas/potatoes/onions/carrots/corn/peas), sugar (granulated or powdered—not brown sugar), Jell-O, and soup mixes (not bouillon). Foods that don't dry pack well include milled grains (such as whole wheat flour/corn meal), nuts, brown rice, barley, sesame, cake mixes, dried eggs, spices, oils, and dried meats.

iii. Refrigerated/frozen foods. Do not advise relying on this, because there may be extended power outages. Generators would use too much fuel for long-term refrigeration use if the grid is down.

iv. Root crop storage. Certainly it's not suggested that everyone has access to a true root cellar. Root crops (potatoes/onions/carrots) could be stored in a deep hole in the ground, covered with straw and then earth. The produce could then be dug out as needed.

v. Natural refrigeration/freezing. A small number of items in waterproof containers (such as waterproof ammunition boxes) with retrieval ropes can be sunk into lakes or rivers. Certainly PQs located in cold winter climates have outdoor freezer space available. Be aware of possible animal scavengers, and package/secure food accordingly.

vi. Precautions against rodents/insects for all types of storage should be paramount. Moisture and high temperatures (above 70 degrees) need to be avoided. Placing desiccants into the dry storage containers helps control moisture, and special packets that absorb oxygen can also be used for longer preservation.

vii. When stored in airtight containers, at cool temperatures, without moisture exposure, these food types have remarkably long useful lives: sugar and wheat (Maximum 20 years); beans, spaghetti noodles and macaroni, dried onions (6-8 years); carrots, fruit drink powders (8-10 years); oats, dry pudding mixes, rice, powdered milk not stored in plastic bags (3 years); white flour (3-5 years); dry soup mixes (4-5 years). Instant potatoes seem to have a shorter life than most things—after about one year, they are questionable.

    b. Fuel storage.

        i. Reserves of fuel are like money in the bank.

        ii. Fuels most important uses are for food preparation and warmth.

        iii. Wood, obviously need to be kept dry.

        iv. Coal should not be stored inside the home; there is a danger of spontaneous combustion. Store coal in a dark shady place, or bury it.

        v. Gasoline fuel (especially with ethanol) will oxidize over time, producing sticky gums, which plug small orifices in motors/stoves/furnaces. There are additives which help reduce this.

        vi. Kerosene is processed to remove materials that form these gums. However, kerosene lamps can emit carbon monoxide and smelly fumes, so caution is needed when using indoors.

    c. Water storage.

        i. Water storage will be necessary with city water sources, in case of system failure. One-gallon plastic milk jugs (well-cleaned) make good drinkable water storage containers. Store eight gallons per person per week, in a cool dark place. Water may need aeration if it's old (pour from jug to jug to restore air into the water). Well-water systems that have an electric pump will need generator back-up, in case the power grid is down. Storage space for water jugs will always be a challenge.

    d. Space needs.

        i. Individuals need personal space of some kind; it doesn't have to be a large area. Urban apartment dwellers will need to be creative. Sleeping and/or eating in shifts may be necessary.

ii. Space expansion strategies include mobile homes/ trailers for rural areas, large wall tents with wood stoves for rural areas in the wintertime, screen houses, tents of any size, hunting shacks, storage units close to you that can be secured (especially for urban apartments), large storage containers/garbage cans/trunks, automobiles can also be used as additional storage space.

iii. Consider space at your PQ or somewhere in the PQC that can be used as a sick bay/trauma area for routine care. An isolation area that is separate and can be kept isolated is imperative. Hopefully, this area will not have to be used. If there is no space other than a room in your apartment or house, use a room with an outside window, so that a fan can be taped to create a negative pressure in room (blowing the air outside). Be aware of where this outside possibly-contaminated air could be blowing. Also, have a door that can be taped.

3. Potential problems at the PQ.

a. Fire risks.

i. Prevention, prevention, prevention.

ii. Have fire extinguishers for A,B,C fire types. Type A is ordinary combustibles (wood, paper, etc.). Type B is flammable liquids such as gasoline, kerosene and alcohol. Type C is electrical fires.

iii. Beware of chimney fires when burning wood, especially if using your fireplace or stove more intensely than in the past.

iv. Discuss fire response plans with the PQC (be sure children have proper instruction).

b. Storage contaminations.

i. Heat, light, insects, rodents, moisture are considered *bad*.

ii. Cool, dark are considered *good*.

iii. Remember that stored water may need to be aerated.

iv. Food storage should be in proper containers and stored in cool, dark areas.

v. Beware of food contaminations as outlined. Rodents can chew through the toughest materials.

c. Water contaminations—if you suspect contamination of this vital resource, refer to section on water disinfection.

d. Entrance of virus to PQ.

i. If someone outside the PQ wishes to join the PQ, they will need to be in the separate isolation area (trailer/tent/similar space) for a period of 7-10 days. This will prevent possible contamination of your PQ with the PI virus. A PQ participant returning from a foray may re-enter without this process if they have strictly adhered to protective barrier discipline.

ii. Urban apartments will have a challenge in this area. (Perhaps an unoccupied apartment could be a central isolation area.)

iii. The isolation trailer, etc., will need to be equipped with essentials, but food, water, and supplies could be delivered to the door.

iv. If someone already within the PQ becomes ill, in any manner that could resemble early PIV, they are immediately moved to the isolation area previously described.

v. Strict adherence to PQC rules should keep these issues to a minimum.

e. Supplies Shortages.

i. Prevention is best here. Having inventory lists for expendable supplies/food/water that are routinely checked by the leader or appointee will help with distributing/rationing supplies.

ii. If foray stores are open and have supplies, and your PQ is in desparate need, one must exercise total barrier protection when leaving the PQ to shop for necessities. No shortcuts can be taken here.

    f. Trauma/sickness.

        i. Although the sick bay/trauma area should be stocked with basic medical supplies, the real answer to trauma lies in prevention. As on an expedition or camping trip, everything is done carefully, especially with sharp objects, fire, heights, tools, chopping wood, etc. There may be nowhere to go for help.

        iii. Pre-establish an emergency provider (EMT, paramedic, nurse, medical doctor, or grandmother) that can be called for instructions when necessary.

    g. Roving troublemakers.

        i. Since everyone could be in the same shape, there's no way to predict who may become a troublemaker.

        ii. Problems could be more prevalent if too many people know that you have stockpiled supplies and are well-prepared for PQ.

        iii. Expect some trouble, and decide how your PQ or PQC should respond to these situations.

        iv. There may still be police units that can respond.

        v. Appropriate signs may be displayed at your PQ, such as PANDEMIC INFLUENZA VIRUS HERE—ENTER AT GREAT RISK, or post a picture of a firearm and write WE CAN'T CALL 9-1-1 ANYMORE.

    h. Desperate relatives or friends make their appearance.

        i. This is more likely the type of people who will be at your doorstep. Engage in conversations from a distance of about 20 feet.

        ii. Perhaps you have some idea who would be likely to fit this scenario, and perhaps you could engage them in discussions regarding your PQs rules. You may learn something.

  iii. Check your food and water supplies, to see if you can spare some for any folks that must be turned away from your PQ. Maybe you have a spare tent and can suggest a place to camp. Also share any up-to-date information you may have.

 i. Job loss.

  i. Regardless of whether or not you entered discussions with your work site prior to entering PQ, you may receive information (if communication systems are still working) stating that you have no job upon your return.

  ii. Discuss all the possible moneymaking opportunities that may be available to you. Choose jobs that could be done during PQ or in the aftermath. Be ready with plans.

  iii. Home mortgages may have to be paid, unless banks and the government exercise appropriate plans for this financial catastrophe. If you are not financially able to cover three-to-six month's of mortgage payments, check with your mortgage company to see if they have any contingency plans. Know your legal rights here.

 j. Death at PQ (not necessarily from PI). This unfortunate event needs to be discussed during the preplanning stage, in order to be handled with care and cause the least amount of stress. Explorers make this type of decision before starting an expedition. "If I die on the ice... slide me into the sea and go on."

4. Financial.

 a. Consider how to decrease your debt now...actively.

 b. Can money be set aside each week/month?

 c. Can you continue to work at home?

 d. Can your present job creatively have you working from home?

 e. Cash at home (in a hidden, fireproof, moisture-proof safety box will be invaluable during the aftermath.

f. Do you have an available financial advisor who understands the Pandemic and its potential problems...or are they just wishful thinkers?

g. Get an appropriate financial advisor, and ask about the safety of your investments. Ask if you need to change anything, and when.

h. Will getting additional insurance now help

(prior to PQ)?

i. How will my mortgage payments be handled?

Check with your mortgage company, and be aware of what is happening at the federal level for potential relief.

j. Can you survive the worst thing that could happen—total collapse of the U.S./World financial systems—or could you survive something less, like a prolonged depression, with the loss of most of your savings, PPSP, and social security?

k. Consider other job possibilities, if the economy's infrastructure can rebound quickly.

5. Communication systems.

a. So important and so vulnerable.

b. Get real. Get a computer and learn how to use the Internet now. It may prove to be the best way to communicate with the most official information sources.

c. Remember, in the most recent crises, cellular telephone use quickly became limited.

d. Can you afford a satellite telephone (expensive)?

e. Are ham radio operators available to you?

f. Radio and television will hopefully remain in service, but may not give official information accurately or quickly.

g. Communication between PQ units within a PQC is vital. Walking may be needed with face-to-face talking, if you are not familiar with smoke signals. Walkie-Talkies may play a role here, as well.

h. Walkie-Talkies for foray times could be quite helpful.

i. A flag system on porches or flagpoles, with predetermined meanings, could be used so drive- or walk-by PQC could know immediate needs. Obviously, if other communication system are available to PQ participants, this would be less helpful.

6. Transportation.

a. Will it be necessary to travel places that are beyond walking/biking distance? Will any of the participants be unable to walk/bike to these areas?

b. Economical use of any gasoline-operated vehicle may be necessary. We already know how to drive more economically, and we may have no other choice but to ration gasoline, if the supply becomes limited or nonexistent.

c. Begin collecting small volumes of gasoline now, in plainly-marked, approved containers.

  i. For gas generators.

  ii. For forays of 50, 100, or 150 miles.

  iii. For four-wheelers.

  iv. For snowmobiles.

  v. For an emergency trip to a hospital/clinic.

d. Keep close inventory of supplies here, as well.

e. If gas stations have available fuel, use precautions.

  i. Glove, mask, gown, shoe covers.

  ii. Spray areas that are handled with 9:1 water:bleach solution, and still use gloves.

iii. Leave the money at the pump.

iv. If needed, communicate from more than 20 feet away.

7. Food Preparation.

a. There may be more laterality in food preparation in a rural kitchen, but not necessarily.

b. Back-up systems are necessary in either rural or urban locations.

c. Remember that boiling can be the cheapest and easiest way to decontaminate water.

d. Barbecue grills could become very important back-up sites, especially with extra canisters of stored propane or bags of charcoal.

e. Microwave ovens may use less resource than other forms of power, such as propane or electric ranges.

f. Camping equipment and stoves with fuel are excellent additional systems.

g. Newer pressure cookers make short work of bulk food cooking (such as beans), and are very safe.

h. Included in this book are just a few bulk food recipes, because most of us have forgotten how to cook like this. Get additional bulk food recipes if you use bulk foods. This will dramatically extend your food supplies.

i. Consider that most of us would be healthier if we ate half as much as we currently consume.

j. Making bread or a similar staple could be a mainstay, and bulk supplies could contribute to this, as well as a bread-making machine for the non-cooks. Making bread can be fun...and the smells...ahh.

k. The Latter-day Saints web site has excellent information on basic food preparation and on bulk foods, in general.

l. Keep a careful running inventory of food supplies (be watchful of pilfering by hungry well-meaning PQ participants. Rationing may need to be instituted at any time. If so, a lot of group discussion will be needed. (Really watch for pilfering during rationing.)

m. Have excellent cook books available and excellent recipes. Talk about a mood elevator—that is the definition of tasty food.

n. Dutch oven cooking is something you might want to explore in Tony Kellar's book on Camping and Cooking With the Bare Essentials.

8. Sick Bay and Isolation Areas.

a. The general scope of these two medical entities will have been discussed in early PQ meetings.

b. These are important considerations, even though hopefully not much used.

c. PQ participants need to know they may have nowhere else to go (certainly nowhere safe to go) for certain severe problems.

d. Check to see how the outside EMS (Emergency Medical Services) systems and hospital systems are doing. Your city may have good triage and surge hospitals and surge clinics, which channel the PI patients, thereby leaving the main hospital free to care for other severe problems (or the severe complications of PI). ("Surge" hospitals and clinics are temporary medical facilities designed to help meet peak needs during the Pandemic.)

e. Having a prescription medical kit at the PQ/PQC can facilitate the handling of more issues.

f. If possible, get a nurse, paramedic, EMT, physician, veterinary technician, veterinarian, or a "doctor grandmother" to be part of your PQC.

9. PQC interactions.

    a. For a PQ Community to function, all members in all participating PQ units must agree to the same rules before quarantine begins.

        i. Regular leader meetings must be held during social isolation time, so that if changes are necessary, everyone is informed and in agreement.

        ii. Fun activities should be planned for all the PQ units together.

        iii. Interaction will allow everyone to get reliable outside news.

        iv. Everyone should be aware of the PQC resources available to them, such as plumbers, baby-sitters, nurses, electricians, excellent cooks, maintenance workers, teachers, etc.

        v. Storage facilities, space, medical supplies should be optimally used, and not unnecessarily duplicated in each unit.

    b. Communication systems have to work well between leaders, and as instantaneously as possible in case of emergencies.

    c. It would be nice to have all PQs within the PQC within walking distance of each other.

10. Fire/police/emergency help.

    a. Depending upon the impact of the PI devastation on the above systems in the "outside world," the PQC may need to help each other in these functions (as able).

    b. Leaders should keep up-to-date on each outside system, and will let each PQ know what is available to them.

11. Children.

    a. Children will have a profound impact on the PI, and especially on the economic consequences of parental work disruption.

b. When PI begins, whether children are in or out of school, the need for parents to be home with them will affect the degree of the parents' job disruption.

School issues will determine the direction of many families.

c. Planning for children in the PQ.

    i. The needs of different age groups.

    ii. The need for good age-appropriate explanations of what is happening and what they can expect.

    iii. The need for periodic time away from their parents during PQ, especially teen-agers.

    iv. The need for children to understand their own reactions to these scary times.

    v. The potential loss of playmates.

    vi. The adolescent issues which may push the rule boundaries.

d. Shared baby-sitting may be helpful.

e. Check the FEMA (Federal Emergency Management Association) web site of emergency management for children (www.fema.gov/kids)

f. Stock surprises, fun activity materials, movie videos and DVDs, etc., so there can be something new/different each week or two.

g. Children should be included in making the PQ work effectively, and can feel that they are an important part of all the activities.

h. Children need to learn good hygiene techniques, and to make them part of their lives (hand washing, sneezing, coughing, etc.).

12. Ethical Issues.

    a. You must feel that the decision to enter the PQ is a positive decision for yourself and your family, and that protecting their health holds priority in your value system.

    b. You must also feel that the PQ/PQC has a positive effect on the overall public health and general good of the public. There is no need to feel guilty if the outside world is in disarray and your group is doing well.

    c. The PQ/PQC process may not be the right choice for people who do not hold these feelings.

    d. If you have a severe health care problem, or a severe complication of PI which requires ICU special care, you may be involved in a decision as to who gets the limited space and equipment at the hospital.

    e. Ethical decisions could arise at the PQ. You can see the need for a wise leader.

        i. Stay in isolation at PQ to die or transfer.

        ii. Food rationing.

        iii. Water rationing.

        iv. Marauders.

        v. Turning away friends or relatives.

13. Leadership. What an important position! No one can take it lightly.

    a. The position must be accepted only after considerable thought. It must be given with even greater thought, democratically.

    b. Often one knows immediately whether or not someone is a good choice for the position.

    c. Necessary leadership qualities have been delineated throughout the book.

        i. Wisdom/common sense.

        ii. Knowledge.

        iii. Listening skills.

        iv. Compassion.

        v. Decision-making capability.

    d. Once the leader has been chosen, follow the leader.

    e. Ongoing leadership duties.

        i. Communicate with other PQC leaders.

        ii. Remain in touch with "outside world."

        iii. Maintain accurate inventories.

        iv. Coordinate the work and the fun flow.

        v. Make the critical decisions.

        vi. Keep regular meetings with PQ.

14. Fun and mental health.

    a. Have pre-made lists, so adequate materials can be stockpiled.

    b. PQC interactions and forays should contribute to sound mental health.

    c. Consider personal enjoyment things you have always wanted to do, to learn, to read, to watch on videotapes or DVDs.

    d. Seek your own personal space, regardless of how big or how small.

    e. Perhaps you may choose to use PQ time for meditation and quiet time, having a spiritual experience, and doing just basic chores.

 f. Now is the time to establish healthy work and play partitions of your day or week. (Like my heroes Helen and Scott Nearing, as reflected in their book The Good Life.)

 g. Also, sleep patterns may be healthier. The return of the siesta may become a real possibility.

 h. Feeling productive and helpful are essential for maintaining mental health (for children, too).

 i. A garden can be an excellent psychiatrist.

15. Spirituality and Religion cannot be left out of the equation.

 a. Everyone's needs must be considered by the leader.

 b. Stock wine, holy water, Bibles/Koran/Book of Mormon/ etc., whatever is needed.

 c. Set aside space for this as appropriate and feasible, in PQ units or in PQC.

 d. TV religious programs, videotapes, books, music may be helpful.

 e. Wooded areas or a city park could be the church many need. Regular church or any such viral-rich gathering is a no-no.

 f. PQ experience could bring a family closer, especially with the happenings in the world outside the PQ acting as a catalyst.

D. Possible PQ-entry sentinel events.

These could also be for specific pre-quarantine events, such as removing children from school, social distancing (no dining out or no public gatherings), and financial planning decisions.

1. WHO (World Health Organization) has begun a *containment* response in a certain area of the world, in order to prevent the spread of a defined PIV (through testing and history of spread among humans). This event may not have significant public reporting, and is not necessarily the admission that the Pandemic has begun.

2. WHO's Director-General makes a public statement that the "last phase change" of a PIV has occurred, and informs the world of such. In other words, the Pandemic has officially begun.

3. CDC reports either 1 or 2 (above), or gives specific advice that the Pandemic has begun.

4. Documentation of any PIV case/s outside of the country of origin.

5. Documentation of certified PIV cases in any country with air/water/rail travel to the United States.

6. First documented case of PIV in the United States.

7. First documented case of PIV in your state.

8. First documented case of PIV in your community.

9. First documented case of PIV in your workplace.

10. First documented case of PIV in your neighborhood or your school.

E. Food and water.

1. General discussion: There is no question which of the two, food or water, is most important to supply. It is water. That is why further in this section, I go into detail on how to disinfect water, in case it becomes necessary to use water from a questionable, possibly contaminated source. However, the first shopping list is a compendium of the various canned, dry boxed, dried, and bottled foods that can be purchased at a supermarket. Not everyone will want or need all that is listed, so use the list as a reminder of your needs.

The amount of food you should purchase for your PQ (determined by projected time in your PQ and by the number of participants), may exceed your purchasing ability. (At least your ability to purchase in one or two shopping ventures.) If the Pandemic holds off for another year, by incrementally beginning now, stockpiling to meet your needs will fare much better. These are items that do not need refrigeration, and if opened, will last without refrigeration for a short length of time. If you have refrigeration and/or freezer space, so much the better. Beware, if the power goes down, so goes your cold food.

If you are prepared and well-stocked, food and water issues become no problem, if the power grids remain intact. The challenges will come with failure of the energy systems that may affect our ability to prepare and store the food, and to deliver our water. Space and cost are often problems, especially with cans, dry boxes, and bottles. The use of bulk products can gain extended food availability and save storage space. That is why a bulk product section is included as a separate list.

Also included are a few simple recipes for using bulk ingredients to make tasty food choices, since many people have forgotten this way of cooking. If storage space and resources are not a problem, cans, dry boxes, and bottles would be the easy way to stock for PQ, even for a full year. In that time frame, with added vitamins and minerals, and adequate supplies of water, there is more than enough nutrition to survive quite well. If handled appropriately, the cans and boxes will not deteriorate in a year's time. Dry boxed goods will do best transferred to sealed storage containers, or coated with paraffin (wax that can be found in the canning/baking section of the supermarket). Another option for meeting extended nutritional demands, much less expensively, although with more anticipated preparation, is using only the bulk foods.

Meals prepared with recipes using only the bulk food list would be a more vegetarian diet, which may not be to your immediate liking, but which would supply complete nutrition when appropriately done.

As you can probably guess, the best compromise on all fronts (expense, space, amounts needed, cooking preparation, etc.) would be to acquire canned, boxed, dried, bottled, and bulk foods together. Tasty, nutritious combinations can then be prepared, and the best space utilization accomplished. I would suggest getting one-half cans/dry boxes/bottles and one-half bulk food items for your proposed length of time in PQ. This should be calculated with a little buffer on the bulk side, just in case.

Suggested amounts of bulk food items per adult individual for six months include

    a. Grains (wheat/rice/corn/oats/spaghetti) —200 lbs.

    b. Legumes/dry beans/peas/lentils —30 lbs.

    c. Powdered milk (minimum equiv. 1 glass/day) —16 lbs.

    d. Sugar —30 lbs.

    e. Cooking oil —5 qts.

    f. Salt —4 lbs.

2. Nutritional and hydration information.

    a. Most people can easily exist on 1/2 the amount of food presently eaten, with an improvement in health. This, of course, excludes certain medical problems. A balanced diet would be nice, but your stockpile may just have "crises diet" capability.

b. You cannot exist on less water than you currently consume.

c. In 70 degree temperatures, most people will die or be close to death in 8-10 days without water (or fluids)—sooner with increased activity or a weakened state of health.

d. A previously healthy adult will survive without water for 2-3 days, in an environmental temperature in excess of 110 degrees.

e. Water is more important than food. Prepare accordingly.

f. If you are perspiring heavily in a high-temperature environment, and you do not have Gatorade (or similar products), stir one-half teaspoon of salt and 4 teaspoons of sugar into one liter of water (about 4 cups). Drink two or three glasses per hour during times of heavy perspiration, to avoid dehydration.

g. If you become dehydrated, with symptoms of weakness, thirst, and little urine volume.

i. Drink 3 or 4 (8-ounce) glasses of Gatorade (or similar products) per hour. (Take small gulps, rather than all at once.)

ii. Or make two solutions, and alternate drinking equal amounts of each: (1) 8-ounces fruit juice, one-half teaspoon honey, pinch of salt. (2) 8-ounces water, one-half teaspoon baking soda.

h. During a two-week time span, an average adult needs 16 gallons of water for hydration and sanitation (brushing teeth and minimal washing). Approximately two-to-three quarts per day for hydration—8 gallons per week is the recommended per person amount to be stored; no more, no less. Storage of more becomes much more difficult.

i. Water can be stored in any airtight, breakage resistant, food grade container. Plastic milk jugs are excellent. They need to be thoroughly cleaned and disinfected before filling. Avoid heat and light during storage. Water can go flat with storage, so aerate it by pouring between containers when used for drinking.

3. Water purification. Drinkable water does not need to be rendered sterile (totally free of germs). It only needs to have the germ count significantly reduced, so that your gastrointestinal tract can do the rest.

Water can be purified for drinking by mechanical, chemical, or physical means through four processes: chemically killing germs; removing germs by filtration; killing germs by boiling; and removing germs and making pure water via distillation. Distilling is perhaps the best method, but not typically practical for our purposes.

I will delve into water purification methods in detail, because of its vital importance to our health and its importance under certain Pandemic scenarios. These are methods you can use for disinfecting water for drinking or cooking, after clarifying the water, as necessary. (Clarifying is removing any particles and small debris before the purification process.)

a. Chlorine chemical methods. Good for killing bacteria and virus (such as H5N1 and its relatives), but not good at killing Giardia, Amoeba, Cryptosporidium, other protozoans, hard core spores, and cysts. However, new chlorine dioxide method works well for all germ forms (see below).

i. Liquid chlorine laundry bleach (Hilex) without additives (such as scents, color-safe, cleaners), 4-6% sodium hypo chlorite. Four drops added to one quart of clear or clarified water (or 16 drops to one gallon), let sit for 30 minutes, will cleanse the water of virus and bacteria. This water is then safe to drink. The purified water should smell of chlorine and have a slight taste of chlorine. This method is great for questionable water sources, other than streams or lakes. To make a surface disinfectant (counter tops/floors/etc.) for H5N1 or PIV, use 9 parts water to 1 part bleach, and spray on surface (example: 1 ounce bleach to 9 ounces water). This water is NOT for drinking or cooking, just for spraying.

—Note—if water is not clarified well or if the water is alkaline, you need to at least double the dose to make water pure enough for drinking.

      ii. Halazone tablets. Five tablets to one quart of clear or clarified water for drinking. Keep the tablet bottle covered tightly, to prevent deterioration of tablets. (Tablets turn yellow and smelly when decomposed.) Halazone tablets are not for spray disinfection purposes; they are not strong enough to act quickly. Halazone has largely been replaced by other methods. -Note—if water is not clarified well or if the water is alkaline, you need to at least double the dose of Halzone.

      iii. Chlorine dioxide method. An excellent new method in tablet form (katadyn micropur purification tablets). The tablets form chlorine dioxide when exposed to water, and produces no taste or odor. Tablets are separately sealed to keep from decomposition. Works in all waters and temperatures, although in cold water, wait four hours for disinfection of all germ types and spores.

    b. Iodine chemical methods. Work well against virus and bacteria, and, if used correctly, against Giardia, Amoeba, protozoa, and most spores and cysts. Methods here are still used by hikers, because they are inexpensive.

      i. Iodine tablets. Tetraglycine hydroperiodide is best. Sold as "Potable Aqua." One tablet to one pint (2 cups) of water, let stand 30 minutes. Has an iodine taste and odor, but not unpleasant. Double standing time if water is cold, and double dosage if water is cloudy. Potable Aqua with "P.A. Plus" additional ingredients improve the taste. Add the P.A. Plus after 30 minutes with Potable Aqua tablet.

      ii. Saturated iodine. Water solution—generally called 2% tincture of iodine. Commercially available as Polar Pure. Add appropriate number of drops, depending on the temperature and clarity of the water (usually 5 drops per quart of water). Let stand 30 minutes. Double the time if the water is cold. Double the dosage if the water is cloudy.

c. Mixed oxidant method. New, easy, reliable for all forms of germs and cysts, if directions are followed. Able to easily treat large volumes of water. Commercially available as MSR Miox Water Purifier, it runs on batteries, creating a small brew of "mixed oxidants," which is added to potentially-contaminated water, causing inactivation of all forms of germs and cysts. You will need to wait up to four hours for everything to be inactivated.

d. Filter methods. Two basic types of filters available.

    i. Screen filters, for filtering larger particulates.

    ii. Ceramic filters. Probably offer the most effective smallest filter. The smallest filter size is 0.2 micron, which will eliminate all bacteria and larger germs, but not viruses. Virus size is much smaller. The addition of silver impregnation to the ceramic filter prohibits bacterial growth, and may have some denaturing effect on viruses, but is not recommended for viral removal. The addition of activated carbon to the filters helps eliminate chemical toxins, and also improves taste. It is important to note that filtration systems need to be used in conjunction with chemically pretreated water (and charcoal for taste), for absolute certainty of total disinfection of all forms of germs and their cysts or spores.

e. Boiling method. A tried-and-true method, easily accomplished when all else fails, or when you have none of the above methods available. It obviously requires energy of some sort to boil the water, so this could be a limiting factor, depending on your circumstances. The rules are:

    i. Boil for 5-10 minutes at sea level.

    ii. Add one minute for each 1,000 feet of elevation.

    iii. This will render the water disinfected for drinking.

    iv. Actually, a temperature of 150 degrees F. for 10-20 minutes will render the water drinkable under most circumstances. Not sterile, but safe to drink.

    v. If short of fuel, the water can be just brought to a boil, rendering it drinkable. Not sterile, but safe to drink again.

4. Shopping List for canned, dry, dried, or bottled food. (A list from which to pick and choose.)

Beverages	Condiments	Cheese
__Coffee	__Mustard, small	__Block, paraffinized
__Tea	__Ketchup, small	__Velveeta
__Tang	__Barbecue sauce, small	__Parmesan, grated
__Kool-Aid	__Tartar sauce, small	__Cheese salsa
__Lemonades	__Soy sauce, small	
__Iced tea	__Worcestershire sauce	Vinegars
__Canned juices	__Chicken broth, canned	__Cider
__Apple cider, dry	__Gravies, canned	__White
__Lemon juice		__Balsamic
	Dressings & Sauces	__Red cooking wine
Oils & Butter	__Salad dressing, small	
__Olive oil, regular	__Miracle whip, small	Baking Ingredients
__Extra virgin olive oil	__White sauce mix	__Yeast, dry
__Canola oil	__Gravy mix, powdered	__Baking soda
		__Corn starch
Spices	Pickles/Olives	__Baking powder
__Marjoram	__Dill pickles	__Powdered butter
__Nutmeg	__Sweet pickles	__Evaporated milk
__Lemon peel	__Green olives	__Sweet. cond. milk
__Parsley flakes	__Black olives	__Powdered eggs
__Minced garlic	__Pickled beets	__Chocolate chips
__Minced onions		__Vanilla
__Taco seasoning	Sugars	__Cocoa, baking
__Chili powder	__White granulated	__Molasses

__Oregano

__Cardamom

__Cinnamon

__Cinnamon sticks

__Basil

__Bay leaves
__Ground cloves
__Coriander

__Caraway seeds
__Dill seed
__Mustard seed
__Curry
__Orange peel
__Paprika
__Rosemary

__Cayenne powder
__Pumpkin pie spice
__Peppercorns
__Sage
__Turmeric
__Thyme
__Celery flakes/seed
__Lemon pepper seas.
__Apple pie spice
__Cumin

Dried Vegetables

__Brown

__Marshmallows

__Frostings, box

__Malted milk powder

__Honey

__Tapioca, dried

Jams/Jellies (small)
__Strawberry
__Raspberry
__Grape
__Blueberry
__Your choice

Canned Fruits
__Peaches
__Pears

__Mandarin oranges
__Pineapple
__Pumpkin
__Fruit Cocktail
__Maraschino cherries

Canned Vegetables
__Sauerkraut
__Green beans

__Sweet peas

__Crisco butter sticks
__Crisco shortening
__Frostings, canned
__Dream whip, powd.

Breakfast
__Cereal, boxed
__Oatmeal

__Cream of wheat
__Granola/bran
__Pancake mixes
__Muffin mixes
__Peanut butter
__Syrups

Dried Fruits
__Figs/dates

__Apricots
__Apples
__Raisins
__Prunes
__Craisons

Boxed Meals
__Hamburger Helper
__Macaroni and cheese
__Potato combo mixes

___(sm pkg, not bulk)

__Split peas

__Lentils

__Navy beans

__Red kidney beans

__Lima beans

__Great northern

Canned Meals

__Baked beans

__Beef stew

__Hash

__Pork and beans

Chips/Crackers

__Tortilla chips

__Potato chips

__Saltine crackers

__Ry Crisp

__Graham crackers

Nuts/Seeds/Mixes

__Peanuts, dry roast

__Almonds, whole

__Cashews

__Sunflower seeds

__Pumpkin seeds

__Corn, whole

__Corn, creamed

__French fried onions

__Kidney beans

__Black beans

__Butter beans

__Diced tomatoes

__Tomato paste

__Tomato sauce

__Spaghetti sauce

__Salsa

__Jalapeno peppers

__Mushrooms

Canned Meats

__Spam

__Salmon

__Tuna

__Chicken

__Shrimp

__Oysters/clams

__Sardines/herring

__Canned ham

__Canned roast beef

__Corned beef

Baby Foods

__Tuna Helper

__Pasta combo mixes

Dehydrated Meals

__Camping meals, any

Soups (basic)

__Chicken noodle

__Tomato

__Cream of chicken

__Cream of mushroom

__Vegetable/beef

__Cheese soup

__Bouillon

__Instant soup, dry

Dry Meats

__Bacon bits

__Bologna, ring

__Pepperoni, sliced

Candies

__Hard candies

__Lemon drops

__Chocoholic types

Special Foods

__Walnuts/pecans

__Popcorn

__Microwave popcorn

__Trail mixes

Pastas

__Spaghetti

__Macaroni

__Lasagna

__Rigatoni

__Shells

__Manicotti

__Egg noodles

__Formula

__Fruits

__Vegetables

__Juices

__Teething biscuits

__Snacks

__Pedialyte

__Gluten-free

__Salt free

__Sugar-free

__Lactose-free

__Other

5. Bulk food supply list and pet foods (amounts needed determined by calculations).

    a. __Sugars, granulated/brown/powdered.

    b. __Milk, instant.

    c. __Potatoes, instant.

    d. __Molasses.

    e. __Rice, white/brown/wild.

    f. __Salt/pepper/selected spices.

    g. __Wheat grain, unground (Red)—for bread or rolls.

    h. __Wheat flour, ground—unbleached for bread and rolls.

    i. __Wheat flour, ground—unbleached soft (White)—for pastries.

    j. __Corn meal.

    k. __Oat bran, rolled.

    l. __Barley.

    m. __Peas.

    n. __Lentils.

    o. __Beans.

    p. __Noodles (all types).

    q. __Pasta/spaghetti.

    r. __Olive oil.

    s. __Extra virgin olive oil.

    t. __Powdered drinks.

    u. __Nuts and seeds.

    v. __Wine.

6. Simple recipes for bulk foods.

EGGLESS, BUTTERLESS, AND MILKLESS CAKE

2 cups brown sugar 1 teaspoon cinnamon
3/4 teaspoon salt 3/4 teaspoon cloves
2 cups hot water 1 teaspoon baking soda
2 Tablespoons shortening 3 cups flour
1 cup raisins

Boil together sugar, salt, water, shortening, raisins, and spices for 5 minutes.
When cold, add flour and baking soda (dissolved in 1 teaspoon of the hot water).
Stir just enough to mix well. Lightly grease
2 loaf pans. Pour batter into pans, and bake at 325 degrees for 45 minutes.
When cool, frost or sprinkle with powdered sugar. This keeps moist for a long
time. There are no eggs in this recipe. This was a Depression-era cake.

RICE PUDDING

1 cup rice Bring to a boil, cover and simmer over low heat for 20 minutes.

Then add:
1/2 cup powdered milk (prepared with water)
1 - 1/2 cups water
1/2 cup sugar
1/2 cup raisins
1 teaspoon cinnamon

(Milk can be substituted for the powdered milk and water, if you have it
available.)
Simmer another 20 minutes, stirring frequently to avoid burning. Cook down to
the right consistency.

OATMEAL RAISIN COOKIES

3/4 cup margarine, butter, or shortening 1 cup firmly-packed brown sugar
1/2 cup granulated sugar 2 eggs
1 teaspoon vanilla 1 - 1/2 cups flour
1 teaspoon baking soda 1 teaspoon cinnamon
3/4 teaspoon salt 3 cups rolled oats (oatmeal)
1 cup raisins

Beat margarine and sugars. Add eggs and vanilla. Beat well. Add dry ingredients and mix. Stir in raisins. Drop by tablespoons onto ungreased cookie sheet. Bake at 350 degrees for 10-12 minutes.

EASY PIE SHELL

1 - 1/2 cups flour plus 2 Tablespoons
1 -1/2 teaspoons sugar
1 teaspoon salt
1/2 cup oil
2 Tablespoons cold milk

Mix all the ingredients in the pie pan. Spread by pressing with a fork or with your fingers. Add a PIE
FILLING of your choice. Bake according to the filling directions.

PIE CRUMBLE TOP

1/2 cup sugar
3/4 cup flour
1/3 cup margarine

Mix together and sprinkle on top of the pie before baking.

SPLIT PEA SOUP

2 - 1/4 cup green or yellow split peas
3 quarts (12 cups) water
1 thick slice ham (diced)
1 cup chopped onions
2 Tablespoons instant chicken bouillon or 2 chicken bouillon cubes
1/2 teaspoon garlic powder
1/2 teaspoon oregano leaves
1/4 to 1/2 teaspoon pepper
1 bay leaf
1 cup diced carrots
1 cup diced celery

Combine all ingredients, except carrots and celery in a large pot. Simmer, uncovered for 1 -1/2 hours. Stir in the carrots and celery. Simmer, uncovered an additional 2 to 2 -1/2 hours, or until soup reaches desired thickness. Makes about 6 servings.

EASY CHILI

Brown together:
1 lb. hamburger
1 medium onion, chopped (or 2 tablespoons dried onion)
1 -1/2 teaspoons salt dash pepper

Add:
1/2 chopped green pepper
1/2 cup chopped celery (if available)
2 cans kidney beans (about 16 ounces), or presoaked 1
- 1/2 cups dried red beans
1/2 to 1 large can (about 46-ounce can) tomato juice
1 to 1 -1/2 Tablespoons chili powder (to taste)

Simmer for one-half hour or more.

MACARONI AND CHEESE

1 - 1/2 cups elbow macaroni
3 Tablespoons margarine
3 Tablespoons flour
2 cups milk
1/2 teaspoon salt dash pepper
1/4 cup minced onion (optional)
2 cups shredded sharp cheese

Cook macaroni as directed; drain. Melt margarine, blend in flour. Add milk.
Cook and stir until thickened. Add salt, pepper, onion, and cheese. Stir until
cheese is melted. Mix sauce with macaroni. Put into greased or buttered 1
- 1/2-quart casserole. Bake at 350 degrees for 45 minutes. Makes 6-8 servings.

BOSTON BAKED BEANS

Soak overnight in cold water:
1 quart navy or pea beans

Simmer in same water until tender (2-3 hours). Drain, saving liquid.

Place in 2-quart casserole:
the drained cooked beans
(optional) 1 pound salt pork (scalded, rind scraped)
or 1 pound bacon, cut
2 slices onion

Combine and mix with beans:
1/3 cup molasses
2 teaspoons salt
1/3 teaspoon pepper
1/2 teaspoon dry mustard

Cover pot. Bake at 300 degrees for 8 hours. (Use reserved liquid, adding a little
at a time, if beans seem dry.)

TUNA HOT DISH

3 - 1/2 cups medium noodles, cooked and drained

Combine with:
1 can cream of celery or cream of mushroom soup (10 - 3/4 ounces)
1 can peas (16 ounces)
1/2 cup milk
1 can tuna fish (6.5 ounces or larger)
salt and pepper (dash)

Pour into greased or buttered casserole dish. Bake at 350 degrees for 30 minutes.

RICE CASSEROLE

1 cup rice
2 cups water Bring to boil. Cover and simmer on low heat for 20 minutes.

Combine and mix with the rice:
1 can chicken or tuna fish (6.5 ounces or larger)
1 small onion, chopped fine
1 can cream of mushroom soup (10 - 3/4 ounces)
1 cup chopped celery or water chestnuts soy sauce (to-taste)

Pour into greased or buttered casserole dish. Bake at 350 degrees for 30 minutes.

THREE-BEAN CASSEROLE

2 cans (16 ounce) lima beans or butter beans (drained)
2 cans (16 ounce) kidney beans (drained)
2 cans (16 ounce) pork and beans
1 pound bacon, cut into small pieces (optional)
1 pound hamburger
1 cup chopped onion

Brown the meat with the onion. Mix meat with the beans.

Combine and add to bean mixture:
1 Tablespoon vinegar
1 Tablespoon prepared mustard
1/2 teaspoon salt
1/2 to 3/4 cup brown sugar

Bake in large casserole or roaster pan at 350 degrees, covered for 30 minutes.
Uncover and bake an additional 30 minutes.

VELVEETA CHEESE FUDGE

Melt in saucepan over low heat:
1/2 pound margarine (1 cup)
1/2 pound Velveeta cheese

Sift together and add to the melted mixture:
2 pounds powdered sugar
1/2 cup cocoa
(The cocoa and powdered sugar MUST be sifted or the fudge will be lumpy.)

Mix well and then stir in:
1 teaspoon vanilla
1 cup chopped walnuts

Pour into a greased cake pan. Spread and cool.

DROPPED BAKING POWDER BISCUITS

2 cups flour
3 teaspoons baking powder
1/2 teaspoon salt
1/4 cup shortening
1 cup milk

Mix all the ingredients. Drop by teaspoon onto greased cookie sheet. Bake at 450 degrees for 12-15 minutes.

WHITE BREAD

1 pkg. active dry yeast
1/4 cup warm water (about 110 degrees)
2 cups milk, scalded
2 Tablespoons sugar
2 teaspoons salt
1 Tablespoon shortening
6 to 6 -1/2 cups sifted all-purpose flour

Soften the yeast in the warm water. Set aside. Combine hot milk, sugar, salt, and shortening. Cool to lukewarm. Sift in 2 cups of the flour; beat well. Stir in the yeast mixture. Add enough of the remaining flour to make a moderately stiff dough. Turn out on a lightly-floured surface; knead until smooth (8 to 10 minutes). Shape into a ball and place in a lightly-greased bowl, turning once to grease surface. Cover and let rise in a warm place until doubled in size (about 1 -1/2 hours). Punch down. Let rise again until doubled (about 45 minutes). Cut dough into two portions. Shape each into a smooth ball. Cover and let rest 10 minutes. Shape into loaves;
place in 2 greased (8 - 1/2 x 4 - 1/2 x 2 - 1/2 inches) loaf pans. Cover and let rise until doubled
(about 1 hour). Bake in hot oven at 400 degrees for
35 minutes or until done. If top browns too quickly, cover the loaves with aluminum foil the last 20 minutes. Makes 2 loaves.

SOME COOKING SUBSTITUTES

1 Tbs. cornstarch = 2 Tbs. flour
1 square (1 oz) chocolate = 3 Tbs. cocoa, plus 1 Tbs. butter
1 whole egg = 2 egg yolks
1 cup sour milk = 1 Tbs. lemon juice or vinegar plus milk to make 1 cup
1 cup milk = 1/2 cup evaporated milk plus 1/2 cup water
1 cup honey = 3/4 cup sugar plus 1/4 cup liquid
1 cup sugar = 1 cup honey/syrup, and reduce liquid in recipe by 1/4 cup (in cakes, substitute honey for only half the sugar)
1 cup brown sugar = 1 cup granulated sugar plus 2 or 3 Tbs. molasses
1 tsp. baking powder = 1/4 tsp. baking soda plus 1/2 tsp. cream of tartar

To Make Sweetened Condensed Milk:
1 cup plus 2 Tablespoons instant dry milk
1/2 cup warm water
3/4 cup sugar Add dry milk to warm water. Mix well. Set in pan of hot water. Stir in sugar until dissolved. Store in refrigerator. (Recipe equals one 14-ounce can sweetened condensed milk.)

SIMPLE BASIC RECIPES

Dry Beans: One pound of dry beans will yield 6 to 7 cups cooked beans.

Soaking and cooking dry beans before mixing them with other ingredients results in beans which are more tender and reduces overall cooking time of the final recipe.

1 lb. dry beans
6 cups water
2 teaspoons salt

Wash the beans; drain. Dissolve salt in water and add beans. Soak overnight.

1 lb. soaked beans
5 cups hot water
2 teaspoons salt

Dissolve salt in hot water and bring to a boil. Add the soaked beans, and boil gently, uncovered. Add boiling water as needed to keep beans covered. Cook until tender. (If you add cool water instead of boiling water, the beans will get tough.)

Cooking Old Dry Beans: One pound of dry beans will yield 6 to 7 cups cooked beans.

1 lb. dry beans
2 - 1/2 cups hot water
2 teaspoons baking soda

Discard any discolored beans. Wash the beans; drain. Dissolve soda in hot water and add beans. Soak overnight. Drain and rinse two times. Cook until tender, about 2 hours. If using pressure cooker, cook about 20 minutes. Adding 1 Tablespoon oil will cut the foam.

Rice: One cup uncooked rice will yield 3 cups cooked rice.

Rice may be boiled in beef or chicken broth. Mix cooked rice with a variety of ingredients, such as mushrooms, sautéed onions, bacon, almonds, grated cheese, chives.

1 cup rice
2 cups boiling water
1 teaspoon salt

Mix rice and boiling water in saucepan. Add salt and bring to a boil. Cover and simmer for 20 minutes. Fluff with fork.

Wild Rice: One cup uncooked rice will yield 4 cups cooked rice.

1 cup wild rice
3 cups water

In medium saucepan, bring liquid to boil. (May add margarine or butter and salt, if desired.) Stir in wild rice, reduce heat and cover. Simmer 55 minutes. Remove from heat. Let stand 5 minutes. Serve.

Powdered Milk:
1/3 cup nonfat dried milk
1 cup water

Mix thoroughly (may add few grains of salt). Refrigerate overnight for best taste. Makes 1 cup.

Old-Fashioned Oatmeal:

1 cup water
1/2 cup oatmeal dash salt

Bring water to boil. Add salt and oatmeal. Cook over medium heat, stirring occasionally. (Cooking times will vary from 1 to 5 minutes, depending on type of oatmeal purchased.)

MEASURE EQUIVALENTS

Gallon	Quart	Pint
16 cups	4 cups	2 cups

Cup	Fluid Oz	Tbs.	tsp	ML	Drops
1	8	16	48	237	
3/4	6	12	36	177	
2/3	5 - 1/3	10.6	32	158	
1/2	4	8	24	118	
1/3	2 - 2/3	5.3	16	79	
1/4	2	4	12	59	
1/8	1	2	6	30	
1/16	1/2	1	3	15	~375

7. Food contamination. Because water is more immediately essential to our survival, its contamination gets more press time. However, there are several important facts to understand about food contamination from germs other than the H5N1 or the PIV. There may not be a safe emergency room available, so take precautions.

a. Types of food contamination with human consequences.

i. Germs that arrive with the food. Examples include pathogenic E.coli in ground meat (hamburger) and salmonella germs in poultry.

ii. Germs that cross-contaminate. Examples include cutting boards used for meat, followed by another food, allowing germ transference to the second food; or bloody meat germs in the water of a cooler used for soda pop.

iii. Germs that are added to food from our hands or mouth. Examples include tuna salad mixed by someone that has a staphylococcal lesion on their hand; hepatitis virus transmitted from a restaurant worker's unwashed hands to our food; or a glass of partially-drunk milk that is left un-refrigerated.

b. Beware of these foods. *Handle with care.*

i. Eggs (salmonella).

ii. Poultry (salmonella).

iii. Hamburger (E. coli).

iv. Milk (Strept. or Staph).

v. Mayonnaise (Staph).

c. Bacteria love to grow in temperatures between 40 - 140 degrees F.

d. Cooler container facts.

i. Beware of cross-contamination. Keep beverages in a second cooler, rather than sharing the food cooler.

ii. Reserve the top area of the cooler for less-problematic foods, since the top area of the cooler will be warmer than the lower section.

iii. Open and close the cooler as few times as possible.

iv. Keep the cooler in the shade.

e. Overcook poultry and hamburger, or use a meat thermometer.

f. Handle wild fowl with gloves.

g. Use a spray bottle of bleach-water mixture (1 part bleach/9 parts water) to spray food preparation surfaces.

F. Expendable supply list (not including food/water/fuel).

Remember your formula: (1/2 Food) + (less Product use) + (double Timeframes) = Conservation of Expendable Resources. Have an inventory list for expendable products, as well. It will help determine use patterns. If toilet paper supplies are down to five rolls for the next three months, use only two squares at a time.

1. __Toilet paper—vital!

2. __Paper towels—can be used in many "pinches."

3. __Paper plates, cups, disposable knives/forks/spoons (saves water).

4. __Batteries—multiple and many. Know your light sources, including recyclable batteries and charger.

5. __Diapers/Depends.

6. __Matches ("strike anywhere" and waterproof).

7. __Candles (long-burning).

8. __Feminine products.

9. __Laundry soap/softener/color-safe bleach (not to be used as drinking water disinfectant because of additives, but it will kill virus bacteria).

10. __Plastic bags with ties (all sizes, from Ziploc food bags to large strong black bags).

11. __Hand disinfectant (approved type 70% ethanol). Larger sizes are available for refilling the carry-around containers.

12. __Duct tape (many rolls).

13. __Antibacterial soap (to be used with hand sanitizer).

14. __Aluminum foil (it's surprising how many useful devices the foil can make).

15. __Plastic wrap (for sealing many things).

16. __Paraffin (for long-term storage, dip boxes in molten wax).

17. __Energy-saving light bulbs/fuses, if necessary.

18. __Wicks/mantles/extra chimneys for kerosene lamps.

19. __Fuels (overestimate calculated amounts)—gasoline, kerosene, propane, lamp oil, charcoal/coal/lighter fluid, and additives to keep gas from cold weather gumming (ethanol mixes especially).

20. __Lumber and building supplies. During PQ isolation, there may be time to complete your projects wish list.

21. __Cash is certainly an expendable supply.

22. __Insect spray and repellants/fly paper/food covers.

23. __Toilet chemicals for outhouses that help decompose body waste. (Can be sprinkled in shallow holes used for "tinkle and duty.") Urban settings can use the chemical to control odor in plastic pails.

24. __Ammunition.

25. __Personal diary/log.

26. __Camera, extra film.

G. Essential equipment list.

What may be essential for you may not be essential for me, and vice versa. Remember that once in PQ, there will not be the luxury of getting a piece of equipment you suddenly find yourself needing. If another PQC member does not have the needed item, you will have to creatively substitute. Search your house and drawers before making new purchases. The following is a complete list; pick and choose as needed.

    1. __Flashlights, many sizes for different purposes (remember batteries). Perhaps a crank flashlight.

    2. __Kerosene (or lamp oil) hanging lantern/s, or the new Petromax lantern, which can burn anything.

    3. __Mantle-type kerosene or lamp oil lantern/s for brighter light. This will help take away cabin fever darkness during the winter.

    4. __Battery-operated radio or crank radio.

    5. __NOAA weather radio with alarm—even in PQ, one needs to be on the lookout for weather emergencies.

    6. __Sharp knives, sharp axe, and sharpening stone, for cleaning game and preparing wood.

    7. __Shovels, large and small. You may have to bury poop or a body.

    8. __Warm blankets, not only for warmth, but also for sealing off a room for heat conservation (have a hammer and nails).

    9. __Sleeping bags. Many may not be enough.

    10. __Manual can openers (ease of operation is helpful).

    11. __Wheat grinder, if using bulk wheat, wild rice, corn, etc.

    12. __Heavy-duty large plastic bags, strong and black. May need to wrap a body or to have a solar-heated water container.

13. __Large buckets—so many uses. Metal buckets could be used for melting snow. Waste containers with foot-operated pedal for cover (for dumping disinfective materials).

14. __Surprises, books, games, etc. for the children.

15. __Extra warm clothes and cool clothes—layers. A house/apartment may have no heat/air conditioning. Also have extra socks and boots.

16. __Fuel storage tanks for propane, kerosene, lamp oil, gasoline (for needed/special forays and for generators).

17. __Generator, gas or propane. May need to keep water pump operational, at least when power grid is down.

18. __Solar panels for selected needs—not as expensive as they once were.

19. __Fire extinguisher/s, ABC type and dry type. Anticipate any type of fire; there may be no fire department to respond. If using wood heat, beware of chimney fires. Get chimney "bombs" for extinguishing them, or have a ladder on the side of the house with water buckets to dump down the chimney.

20. __Resource books: medical/cooking/homestead skills/etc.

21. __Computer with Internet access.

22. __Compass and maps of possible foray areas.

23. __Backpack/day pack for forays to non-viral areas, in addition to a Barrier Device Pack.

24. __Fishing/hunting/camping equipment for special forays (license if appropriate).

25. __Wild game cleaning and cooking book.

26. __Safe for cash and important papers (fireproof and waterproof).

27. __Complete tool kit: hammer and nails, as well as an assortment of pliers, wrenches to turn off the utilities or to accomplish a multitude of other uses.

28. __Plastic sheeting, for closing less-used rooms and multiple other uses.

29. __Duct tape, many rolls. Remember there are 1,000 uses.

30. __Sewing kit. Repair buttons, zippers, fabric tears.

31. __Bread-making machine, especially for urban dwellers.

32. __Food saver. Can make food supply extend itself.

33. __Chain saw with extra oil, blade, sharpener. Wood saw with sharpener.

34. __Garden tools. Although there are many gardeners who will be able to at least generously supplement their diets with fresh produce, we should not depend on gardening for any or all of our food supply. For the urban dwellers with no yard to till, "earth boxes" on the deck might produce occasional salad ingredients.

35. __Fishing equipment and license, when supplementation is possible.

36. __Hunting equipment and license, when supplementation is possible.

37. __Camp cooking stoves with extra gas or propane, or portable charcoal grill. You never know when this might be the only way to prepare a meal at the homestead.

38. __Dutch oven (large cast iron kettle with lid). Has multiple uses for cooking, and can be used in an outdoor fire pit.

39. __Fans.

40. __Cash, a very comprehensive and versatile tool.

41. __Non-electric kitchen appliances.

42. __Walkie-Talkies, for forays and other "mischief."

43. __Rainwater collection system.

44. __Dry food storage containers, all sizes.

45. __Rope, several sizes/types. Multiple uses.

46. __Long, heavy-duty indoor/outdoor extension cords, to reach trailers or tents on the property, as well as many other uses.

47. __Portable kit or bag containing everything needed for protection (mask, gown, goggles, gloves, hair and shoe covers, hand sanitizer). Must be able to find this at a moment's notice.

48. __Rain gear.

49. __Extra tents, if possible, a large canvas-wall tent and wood stove.

50. __Trailer home. For many uses, not the least of which is a "transition residence" for people entering PQ from viral-rich environments. Individuals would stay here for 7-10 days (past the incubation period of a PIV).

51. __Extra plastic gallon-sized milk containers, washed and dried for collecting water if and when necessary.

52. __Pressure cooker; may save time and energy.

53. __Signal devices for PQ community, aerial flares, smoke flares.

54. __Measuring spoons and cups.

55. __Urinals/Chamber pots, for night time bathroom use.

56. __Extra spray bottles, such as Windex or shower spray, for disinfecting surfaces (9:1 bleach mixture).

H. Medical lists.

1. Over-the-counter medical list. Give a copy of your medical list to a health care provider that you can call for medical advice.

a. __Thermometer, oral and rectal (could be helpful in a diagnosis).

b. __New Basic Life Support guidelines, especially new 2006 CPR instructions, in case the emergency response system could respond to a heart problem. Now that new guidelines are available for AEDs (Automatic External Defibrillators), you may be able to inexpensively secure the older model.

c. __Bandages/steri-strips, variety of types, including knuckle type.

d. __Digital blood pressure device.

e. __Safety razor and blades.

f. __Medicine droppers.

g. __Medicine cups.

h. __Tongue depressors/pocket flashlight.

i. __Sterile Q-tips.

j. __Zip-closure plastic bags, several sizes.

k. __Tape, variety of type (some hypoallergenic).

l. __Safety pins and metal paper clips, all sizes.

m. __Bandanas (like duct tape, are useful for a thousand things).

n. __Adaptic or Telfa nonstick wound pads.

o. __Moleskin.

p. __Spenco 2nd Skin.

q. __Wooden clothes pins or similar, for nose bleed clamps.

r. __Duct tape.

s. __Cotton balls.

t. __Ace bandages, 2" and 6" (3 of each).

u. __Coban wrap, 4" (at least 4 rolls).

v. __Gauze pads, 4" square.

w. __Eye gauze patches.

x. __Irrigating syringes for wounds.

y. __Plastic bags, tie-sealed, for waste disposal/vomit bags.

z. __Water disinfection tablets, such as Potable Aqua with PA Plus or Micropur tabs.

aa. __Paramedic scissors.

bb. __Splinter forceps (like fine-tipped jeweler's forceps).

cc. __Tincture of benzoin bottle, to make any tape stick better and longer.

dd. __Telfa nonstick dressings.

ee. __Rolls of Webril and Kling.

ff. __Splints to be fashioned at home, with materials like cardboard wrapped with duct tape.

gg. __Betadine solution or swabs.

hh. __Alcohol swabs (individually wrapped).

ii. __Antibacterial soap.

jj. __Hand sanitizer (many small containers can be refilled from stock supply, so everyone can carry their own).

kk. __Mosquito and tick repellents.

ll. __Aspirin, 325 mg and 81 mg tablets.

mm. __Ibuprofen, generic 200 mg tablets.

nn. __Naproxen, generic 250 mg tablets.

oo. __Acetaminophen/ASA/caffeine tablets (brand is Excedrin; generic is fine).

pp. __Acetaminophen tablets, extra strength 500 mg.

qq. __Pseudoephedrine tablets, 60 mg (brand is Sudafed; generic is fine).

rr. __Nyquil, bottled.

ss. __Neosynephrine nasal spray, 1/4%

tt. __Diphenhydramine capsules, 25 mg (brand is Benadryl; generic is fine).

uu. __Dramamine tablets, 25 mg.

vv. __Hall's Fruit Breezers cough lozenges.

ww. __Listerine (or generic) mouthwash.

xx. __Milk of Magnesia.

yy. __Multivitamins with minerals and iron. With a balanced diet, probably not needed, but can a Pandemic diet be well-balanced?

zz. __Immodium AD tablets (slows diarrhea and decreases cramping).

aaa. __Pepto Bismol tablets (for diarrhea; in large amounts can be antibacterial).

bbb. __Antacids for gastritis or heartburn (Ultra Tums tablets, Maalox, Mylanta, or generic).

ccc. __Pepcid AC, 10 mg tablets, for gastritis or heartburn.

ddd. __Gas-X tablets, if significant belching problem and discomfort.

eee. __Beano tablets (if you're planning lots of beans in your diet).

fff. __Lactaid tablets (for milk-intolerant participants).

ggg. __Gatorade, available in many flavors (good oral hydration solution).

hhh. __Nix and Rid (for lice or scabies).

iii. __Hydrocortisone cream (1%), generic steroid.

jjj. __Rhuderm lotion (anti-itch for poison ivy and others).

kkk. __Bacitracin ointment (antibacterial ointment).

lll. __Lotrimin cream (1%), for fungal infections.

mmm. __Pure Aloe skin lotion, for sunburn and burns.

nnn. __Zinc oxide ointment, protective skin ointment.

ooo. __Sunscreen, at least #30 protection (preventive).

ppp. __Sunglasses, UV protective (preventive).

qqq. __Aveno oatmeal bath lotion (for soaking itchy and irritated skin).

rrr. __Arm & Hammer bicarbonate of soda (many uses, as well as soaking itchy, irritated skin).

sss. __Oil of cloves (for tooth root exposure).

ttt. __Dental cement (for broken tooth).

uuu. __Dental wax (for broken tooth).

vvv. __Super glue (for irritating small cuts on extremities).

www. __Anti-yeast vaginal suppositories.

xxx. __Anusol hemorrhoidal cream or suppositories.

yyy. __Vicks VapoRub, for boiling water steam inhalations.

2. Prescription Medical Kit for PQ. May have to pay out-of-pocket. Your medical doctor needs to know your allergies and sensitivities. The number and dose of your medicine is up to your physician. Your doctor or health care provider needs this list, so

that if you call with a problem, they know what medications you have available.

    a. __Tamiflu, anti-viral for influenza (5-day supply).

    b. __Pneumonia antibiotics (Z pak or Levaquin, 500 mg tablets).

    c. __Other infections:

        i. __Keflex, 500 mg tablets.

        ii. __Cipro, 500 mg tablets.

        iii. __Septra **DS** tablets.

        iv. __Augmentin 875 tablets.

        v. __Doxycycline 100 tablets.

        vi. __Flagyl, 500 mg tablets.

    d. __Pain medications.

        i. __Percocet 5/325 tablets—addictive potential.

        ii. __Darvocet N 100 tablets—addictive potential.

    e. __Anxiety, Ativan tablets, 1 mg—addictive potential.

    f. __Allergy/Asthma, epi pens (4 adult and 4 junior).

    g. __Steroids.

        i. __Medrol Dos Pak, powerful oral steroid in tapering dose.

        ii. __Triamcinalone actetonide cream, 0.1% (for skin "reactivity").

    h. __Nausea (Phenergan tablets 50 mg, or Phenergan suppositories 50 mg).

    i. __Cough (Tessalon pearles).

    j. __Eye medications.

        i. __Tetracaine eye drops, anesthetic drops.

ii. __Gentamycin eye drops, antibiotic.

iii. __Homatropine eye drops (2%), dilates eye/can help reduce eye pain in certain problems.

k. __Cetacaine spray, for numbing mucosal surfaces.

l. __Birth control pills, for special circumstances.

m. __Sterile bottles of saline, when boiled water is not convenient.

n. __Suture kit with suture (includes needle holder, hemostats, and cup holders).

o. __Plaster impregnated strips or rolls for fashioning splints.

p. __Tegaderm, clear sterile plastic adhesive film over skin avulsions (many uses).

q. __Foley catheters, straight (for emptying bladder—coude tip).

r. __Lidocaine jelly (4%), skin and mucous membrane anesthetic.

s. __Ethylene Chloride, skin freeze spray (an ice cube can also work).

t. __Diabetic supplies, if appropriate.

3. Personal hygiene list.

a. Remember that 6-12 months is a long time.

b. So much of this is personal choice, that a list is for you to make. Don't forget dental supplies.

c. Most of the items here could be used in half quantities, from what we usually use. This would reduce costs.

d. Don't forget condoms or other birth control devices. Within a 6-12 month period, you could deliver a baby and have no prenatal care. Of course, abstinence is always a choice. What we have learned from other catastrophes (such as power blackouts) is that there are many more births nine months later.

e. With long isolation periods, sometimes there is a positive mental uplift to "clean up" and "doll up." Don't forget your cosmetic needs.

4. List of "natural" products claimed to have effect with influenza. To be complete, the folk medicines and herbal medicines need to be listed. No guarantees are provided on the product or the research to support their use.

—Please note—these are probably worth avoiding if sick with pandemic influenza: honey, chocolate, echinacea, kimchi (all of which increase the bad cytokines); also dairy products and bananas, which increase mucous production.

a. __Garlic (allicin), anti-viral ("Louie swears by it").

b. __Oscillococcinum, "diluted" flu virus.

c. __Grape juice, contains resveratol (antioxidant). Claim: inhibits reproduction of flu viruses by inhibiting neuraminidase.

d. __Vitamin C. Claim: blocks neuraminidase and may decrease inflammatory cytokines. Remember, Tamiflu works by inhibiting neuraminidase.

e. __Cold packs instead of Tylenol or aspirin. They may prolong the infection by dropping temperature.

f. __Sexual activity may increase immunoglobulin A production, a possible flu fighting antibody. (Beware of immunoglobulin A "toxicity.")

g. __Apple juice, anti-viral, especially the pulp and skin.

h. __Sauerkraut, anti-viral and acclaimed by many.

i. __Selenium, helps diminish oxidative stress during flu.

j. __Cranberry juice, may have some anti-viral activity, as well as keeping bacteria off urinary tract walls.

k. __Skullcap (scuttellaria), an herb used as a tea. Claim: may be anti-viral by inhibiting neuraminidase.

l. __St. John's Wort (hypericun). Claim: anti-viral, also decreases dangerous cytokines.

m. __Green tea. Claim: the inexpensive rival of Tamiflu, by inhibiting neuraminidase and decreasing cytokines.

n. __Cat's Claw (uncaria tomentosa). Claim: decreases cytokines and boosts immunity, but not to be used in children or pregnant females.

o. __Curcumin (turmeric spice). Claim: decreases cytokines, but take with food. Not advised for pregnant females or nursing mothers.

p. __Astragalus root (astragali radix). Claim: immune booster, non-specific.

q. __Tea tree steam inhalations. Claim: reduces cytokines, relieves congestion.

5. Barrier devices. —Note: remember when disrobing from all your protective devices, to remove your gloves last, so you don't transfer the virus onto your bare skin from the surface of your barriers during the disrobing process. All disposable pieces need to be placed in a decontamination beg (heavy-duty plastic), specially marked, to be burned later. Articles that can be disinfected by spraying (9:1 or 5:1 bleach solution) or dipping, will need 30 minutes for virus killing time to be complete. If you do the barrier procedures well, you should be protected when exposed to a viral-rich environment—*but it takes discipline!*

a. __Gloves. Supply of vinyl or latex gloves, disposable type. Rubber dishwashing gloves could be used if they are fully dipped in 9:1 bleach solution in a large pail. (Hold in fluid for 30 seconds.) The pail can be kept covered, so the solution can be used multiple times. The disposable gloves are much more convenient. The virus does not enter the body through your hands; but is transferred from your hands to your eyes, nose, or mouth, or to someone or something else.

b. __Gowns. Be creative. They could be rain gear that can be sprayed with disinfectant after each use. They could be made of fabric that can be washed in 9:1 bleach water. If bulky, one could put rubber bands around arms and legs.

c. __Hair covers. Shower caps or, better yet, the new food covers with elastic bands (if you can find them in stores) work well. Remember that germs could land in your hair and be easily transferred to your mucosal surfaces by your hands.

d. __Foot covers. To prevent picking up the germ from walking surfaces, place plastic bags over shoes or boots and affix with rubber bands. Walking surfaces are viral-rich areas, because the suspended viral particles in the air from a cough will eventually land on some surface.

e. __Masks. The mask that is the most effective and is the least prohibitive in cost is the 3M N95 Mask. It is not a perfect protection, but is better than looser fitting single masks. The 95 refers to 95% effective in its ability to filter viruses from your breathing space. If you are in a viral-rich "aerosol" environment, the virus particles will adhere to the outer surface of the mask. One has to be wary of this surface. The 9:1 bleach spray should help disinfect it, but it might be more appropriate to just destroy it at the end of the exposure. If you do not have the N95 type, but the other simpler 3M Mask that resembles it, just staple two masks together, one over the other. This would give a similar filtration effect and similar 2-banded head straps. Use non-allergenic tape around the edges of the inner mask, and tape to your face for a seal. A piece of cut sponge across the inner mask's nose bridge helps further seal the nose area.

f. __Goggles. Your eyes have mucosal surfaces around them. We know mucosal surfaces are potential entry points for the influenza germ. There are not as many sialic acid-hemaglutinin binding sites as there are lower in the respiratory tract. However, virus particles lying on a surface can be picked up on your hand and transferred to your eyes, nose, or mouth, and are as equally capable of beginning a human influenza infection as are the virus particles that are breathed into a lower portion of your respiratory tract. Perhaps the latter is a more effective way of transferring the infection, but not the only way. The goggles, therefore, cover important entry points. The skin over our bodies is a very effective barrier to entry of the influenza virus. The goggles can be sprayed or disinfected by dipping in the bleach solution. Tight-fitting glasses with side barriers could also be used, but swimming goggles may fit the bill the best.

g. __The ultimate barrier device is Preventive Quarantine, that imaginary line barrier of total social isolation around your PQ and/or PQC.

6. Pandemic barrier kit for forays.

a. __Day pack for containing materials.

b. __Attached bleach spray bottles (1 or 2).

c. __Masks, 3M N95 or fashioned types as substitutes (5).

d. __Goggles, tight-fitting (swim goggles work best).

e. __Gloves, vinyl preferred (or large dishwashing gloves).

f. __Hair protector, disposable.

g. __Gowns, rain coats that can be sprayed with bleach spray. Some may supply head cover; use rubber bands to secure sleeves and legs. Other types of gowns need to be specially washed.

h. __Strong plastic bags, for shoe wrap with rubber bands.

i. __Non-allergenic adhesive tape, to seal mask edges.

j. __Bottle of Potable Aqua tablets, or Tincture of Iodine (2%) 5 drops per quart of water.

k. __Disposable plastic bag (large, strong), for contaminated equipment used above that can't be easily disinfected.

l. __Optional, depending on space, one 2-quart container to make disinfecting solution with above iodine or bleach solution.

m. __Tamiflu, the "in case" possibly helpful anti-viral drug (follow directions for use).

7. Disinfectants for H5N1 or PIV. H5N1 or PIV can be easily killed by appropriate use of effective products. Vigilance to do the disinfection properly is the more critical factor.

Some definitions are in order here.

Disinfectant: solution to kill disease germs by a chemical agent (does not affect spores). Example 9:1 or 5:1 water/bleach solution will kill H5N1 and PIV.

Antiseptic or Bacteriostatic: solution that inhibits growth and development of dangerous germs, and can also act as a disinfectant if certain agents or concentrations are used. Example: Honey is a natural antiseptic solution.

a. Types of disinfectants for H5N1 and PIV.

i. Sanitizer solutions. Kills bacterial germs

(not spores), but may *not* kill all virus.

ii. Bactericidal solutions. Kills bacterial germs.

iii. Virocidal solutions. Kills virus germs.

b. Hand sanitizers, gel form. Usually 62-70% ethanol, with isopropyl alcohol and hand soothing ingredient. Hand sanitizers can be placed in small squeeze containers that can be carried on your person, making hand rinsing convenient. They can be refilled from stock supply. Sanitizers are bacteriocidal, but not completely virocidal. The alcohol may denature or desiccate some of the virus. Combined with soap washing, it is certainly an antiseptic approach. That's why gloves are necessary. Combining wipes with gel and washes with soap and water will wash the virus from your skin. Wash after glove use as well.

c. Spray bottles of 9:1 dilution 6% Sodium Hypo-chlorite (Hilex bleach) with water is also an effective disinfectant for influenza germs on surfaces. Some sources say 5:1 ratio water/bleach might be more effective, but most experts feel that 9:1 is strong enough. It takes approximately 30 minutes for the killing to be complete, depending on the temperature. There is some indication that the hypo chlorite spray is not as effective on metal surfaces as it is on other surface types. Perhaps on metal surfaces, the 5:1 ratio would be more effective. This solution is too harsh for skin surfaces on any regular basis. You could have two dilutions of spray bottles (remember to accurately and boldly label all solutions). Influenza particles exist in water for several days; longer if the water is cold. Influenza particles also stay infectious on plain surfaces for at least 24 hours. Wash basins used by PIV victims are a source for viral contamination. Solutions of chlorine will kill the virus if in the correct concentration and/or with sufficient time exposure to the chlorine. If using chlorine to disinfect your drinking water, it should have a slight chlorine taste. It also should set for at least 30 minutes, longer in cold water. If water is more contaminated, double the dose of chlorine. Municipal water supplies should generally be safe, if there has been no contamination. Beware of excessive chlorine in your septic system—it may be rendered ineffective.

d. Betadine hand solutions. 7.5% povidine-iodine solution. This solution is both bactericidal and virocidal, and could be considered a hand disinfectant, in contrast to the 70% hand gels.

e. Boiling water. High surface heat will kill H5N1 or PIV.

f. Disinfecting contaminated clothing. Wash in any bleach solution.

g. Your clothes dryer alone on *high* heat for about 45 minutes can also kill virus, when there is a scarcity of water. Dryer temperatures vary, but the average low temperature is 110 degrees, medium temperature is about 155 degrees, and high temperature is up to 200 degrees. Dryer use takes considerable electrical power.

8. Disposal of contaminated materials. Assuming they are appropriately bagged and labeled "disposable contaminants" (not needles, syringes, or sharps).

    a. Burn, baby, burn! Choose a safe place; H5N1 can't survive the fire.

    b. Certain equipment need not be set aside and not used again, just spray or dip it.

9. Medical history form for each PQ member (and for each unit of PQC).

10. Telephone call list to post (if fortunate enough to have telephone service).

I. "Gosh, Darn, Heck!!" scramble list.

For those who have only days to prepare—what is critical if you can find it. The list is the same for urban or rural dwellers.

1. Food.

a. Any and all you can get. Preferably canned, dried, bottled, dry boxed goods.

b. Bulk items will be less in demand—check for them immediately.

c. If you're lucky enough to get them, fresh root crops can be buried with straw in a makeshift root cellar.

d. Storage facilities will be less of a problem than obtaining food choices, but have some idea of where you can stock your supplies.

e. Baby food? Pet food?

f. Be prepared to eat much less than usual, for an extended period of time—ration.

2. Water.

a. If you have your own well and back-up generator, you needn't worry. If not, get containers.
You can fill them later.

b. If you are an urban dweller, get as many containers as possible. You can fill them later.

c. If you can purchase and afford bottled water, that's fine. Get as much as you are able.

3. Fuel.

a. Camp stove fuel, if you have camp equipment to use for cooking. Or grill fuel, such as propane tanks.

b. Fill your car/s gas tank/s, and as many spare tanks as available.

c. Kerosene, if you have appropriate lanterns.

d. Charcoal and starter fluid.

4. Expendibles.

    a. Toilet paper, paper towels.

    b. Batteries for flashlights/radio.

    c. Duct tape/rope, all sizes.

    d. Aluminum foil.

    e. Matches/candles.

    f. Bleach (Hilex plain), several gallons.

    g. Plastic bags, all sizes.

    h. Specific children's needs, such as diapers.

    i. Wipes, with aloe.

5. Equipment.

    a. Flashlights.

    b. Portable radio.

    c. Manual can opener.

    d. Buckets/storage containers of all types.

    e. Minimal tool kit.

    f. Camp equipment—cooking stoves/ovens/small grill (especially for urban PQers).

    g. Fan/s.

    h. Spray bottles for bleach solutions.

    i. Hand sanitizer and antibacterial soap.

6. Medical supplies.

    a. Extra prescription medicines—call MD and pharmacy; may need out-of-pocket money. Get a three month supply or more if possible.

    b. Extra special supplies, such as diabetic testing equipment.

    c. Any barrier devices left in stores, especially masks and gloves; dishwashing gloves at least.

    d. Over-the-counter medical supplies.

    e. Condoms, if appropriate.

J. Grab list for a PQ participant who must leave fast and come a distance to the PQ.

Should all fit in one pack.

1. Cash/check books/account numbers/passport/driver's license.
2. Credit card/s.
3. Energy bars or similar calories that don't have to be heated.
4. Bottled water—lots of it.
5. Gloves, masks.
6. Spray bottle 9:1 bleach solution (filled). Beware of leaks.
7. Hand sanitizer/soap.
8. Rain gear/warm jacket.
9. Important papers.
10. Important telephone numbers.
11. Cellular telephone.
12. Prescription medications/over-the-counter medicines you use.
13. Change of clothing.
14. Book/s.
15. Matches.
16. Flashlight and batteries.
17. Toilet paper.
18. Portable radio.
19. Knife, plastic dishes/cups/silverware, can opener.
20. Plastic bags, large and small.
21. Duct tape.
22. Wipes with aloe, for hygiene.
23. Toothbrush and toothpaste.

V. PQ SOCIAL ISOLATION PERIOD

A. General rules for a PQ.

1. Rules are set at the first meeting, with all PQ participants in attendance.

2. First, choose a leader, if you have not already done so. The leader will then lead the meeting.

3. Rules need to be simply stated, and not complicated.

4. The most important concept at the PQ: the PIV must not get across the ultimate barrier protection line.

5. Entry to PQ (the ultimate barrier protection) begins at the sentinel event (to be decided). Regardless of what one is doing, within 24 hours of the sentinel event, the participants need to be gathered at the PQ. Obviously, extenuating circumstances are allowed for travel time.

6. Decide which sentinel event to choose, with total agreement. Hereafter, participants have the duty to keep track of these events.

7. General assignments of tasks are made, which can vary from time to time, and other duties getting ready for the PQ. Formulation of supply list needs and then begin supplies acquisition, and many other preparatory functions needed at the PQ.

8. Basic rules of conduct at the PQ, once started.

    a. No one enters from outside PQ (including neighbor's pets). Signs appropriately posted.

b. Mail is specially handled. Gloves.

c. Cars are specially handled (signs posted).

d. If someone from a viral-rich area comes to the PQ, the leader will house them in the isolation trailer/tent/etc., for 7-10 days, before they may enter into the main PQ.

e. The leader determines forays of any kind.

f. If and when PQC is established, participants can move freely between units within the same PQC

(this is not considered a foray).

g. Each individual has a personal barrier protection kit with them (or close by) at all times, and knows how to use it. The leader is responsible for teaching participants how to use it.

h. Children are the responsibility of their parents.

i. The leader is in charge of all inventories.

j. Everyone need to be at the weekly PQ meetings, or communicate together every week.

k. After group discussions, the leader has the final decision regarding any significant question, once the PQ has begun.

l. Further rules will be decided as the PQ unfolds.

B. General rules for a PQ Community.

1. Every PQ agrees on the same rule structure and the same entering sentinel event, and pledges adherence to the rules of isolation and honesty in communications.

2. Any PQ unit can opt out at any time, if other members are given proper notice.

3. Have fun together and mutually support each other in every possible way.

4. All PQ leaders agree to regular meeting times.

5. If any significant information becomes available, or mistakes are inadvertently make, everyone agrees to immediately share the information, if it is potentially for the good of everyone.

C. How to deal with potential PIV exposures or actual exposures.

1. People exposures. If a person is encountered inadvertently or intentionally at the PQ or on a foray.

   a. Maintain a distance of 20 feet, as able. Certainly come no closer than 10 feet.

   b. Use barrier device kit appropriately. In certain instances, only mask and gloves may be needed. Other instances may require full barrier protection.

   c. Do *everything* to minimize any close contact of fewer than 10 feet.

   d. If for some reason you become significantly exposed to an individual (such as a handshake or a cough), and you are not wearing protective barrier equipment, this information must be immediately reported to your leader. Make no physical contact with anyone or anything in your PQ unit. You will need to be isolated away from the main PQ for 7-10 days. You will also need to take Tamiflu, if it's available.

2. Forays. Any leaving of the main PQ for whatever reason (fun to non-viral rich area, essential professions, absolute supply need, etc.).

   a. Depending on the environment you are entering, you will need to keep the ultimate barrier protection concept in mind, and use all of the barrier protection equipment in your kit (mask, gown, hair cover, goggles, gloves, shoe covers, and attachments). If you are going to a viral-poor area (such as a forest), you may not "dude up" in any gear. *These are critical decisions that cannot be taken lightly.*

　　b. This type of approach to any potentially viral-rich area can be used effectively in the urban environment, as well. In the urban environment, your barrier kit is a constant travel companion, and must be used almost reflexively. Early stockpiling of barrier supplies is critical for an urban individual, since they will likely have more need of them.

　　c. Forays always need to be pre-approved by the leader.

　　d. Upon returning from foray, before entering the PQ, disrobe from your barrier gear as described (remember to remove gloves last), and place any contaminants in a plastic bag, for later incineration. If anything else has been significantly exposed, spray it with the bleach solution (example: the car was touched by someone).

　3. Mail.

　　a. Mail could be handled in many ways, if the service is at all still available.

　　b. It is a potential "fomite" (something that inadvertently carries a germ).

　　c. Exposed to sunlight and summer heat for 3-4 days would probably kill any H5N1 or PIV.

　　d. Mail could be heated in the oven at 220 degrees for 10 minutes. Beware of fire.

　　e. Keep in mind that the inside of the mail could be just as contaminated as the outside.

　　f. The microwave oven might be used, but not knowing if the inside of the letters or packages contain foil or similar, would make plan unwise.

g. The best way is to wear gloves for sorting and opening. Any particular letter or piece that could be set aside for further action, could be set aside for an extended period of time, or heated.

h. Dispose of the gloves.

4. Vehicles entering the PQ.

a. All vehicles must be considered fomites, unless it is your vehicle from a known viral-poor foray.

b. With all other vehicles, remain at least 20 feet away while you inquire as to the reason they have come to the PQ.

c. Ask the purpose of the visit, and direct them to leave as soon as possible.

d. Use the barrier kit as needed, if there are other contingencies.

e. Post appropriate signs at the entrance to the driveway, telling anyone entering "what it's all about."

5. Pets, wildlife, flies, mosquitos. All could be fomites or actually infected with H5N1. Animals may still carry the H5N1 virus, and could still transmit it to humans. So be cautious, but not paranoid. This will happen after the H5N1 reaches North America this year.

a. Wild fowl, ducks (geese and swans would be dead, but could have infected the water).

b. Cats, dogs, ferrets, tigers, pigs, and who knows which other animals. Dogs and cats might carry the PIV as a fomite from their sick or dead master. They need to return home pronto.

c. Any special pets at the PQ need to be leashed or fenced to prevent wandering and possible acquisition of H5N1.

d. Flies have been reported to carry H5N1 as a fomite. Fly paper may be less toxic than fly sprays. Mosquitos have not been known to carry influenza viruses. Remember that West Nile Fever is still spreading, though. Keep a supply of Ultrathon or similar insect repellant handy.

Lyme Disease and Babiosis are spread by ticks, and when spending time outdoors, it would be wise to take tick protection seriously.

D. Medical Strategies.

1. General considerations.

a. It's important to note here that the PQ may need to function as an emergency room, hospital, hospice or nursing home.

b. There is no reason a complete medical kit can't be adequately employed by a non-health care professional through instructions over the telephone;

at least on an emergency basis when there are no other choices.

c. PQs with a nurse, EMT, or medical doctor will be able to function more effectively than a lay person in a medical situation, but that luxury may not be available.

d. Many standard approaches to medical care will be changed by the potential immensity of the problems here with PI.

e. Call the regular system for emergency response if truly needed, but don't be discouraged if there happens to be no answer.

2. Space considerations.

a. Each PQ or PQC will need a separate trailer, tent, room, cabin, shack, or tree house for isolation.

Individuals coming from a viral-rich environment have significant potential of PIV, even though they appear healthy at the moment. Every entering individual must be isolated for 7-10 days. The isolation area needs to be fully equipped with living capability. Meals/water/supplies can be carefully delivered to them. Perhaps leaving items in a designated pickup area at a predetermined time/s of day. If there has been no sign of illness by the seventh day, the likelihood of PI is extremely remote.

b. A sick bay area will be needed for treating regular medical or trauma problems.

3. General medical or trauma considerations.

a. Prevent, prevent, prevent.

b. Be careful of other infectious agents that could be spread by sloppy hygiene.

c. The definite answer in trauma is prevent, prevent, prevent. With slower speeds and less traffic, perhaps the serious trauma accidents will be down. There may be no place for them in the hospital system, anyway.

d. Heart attacks, strokes, GI bleeds and similar will still happen, and it will be a flip of the coin as to whether the hospital systems will be able to help.

e. On an encouraging note, if the Pandemic tarries and allows a sufficient length of time for planning at the local medical levels, the power of grass root creativity and ingenuity could make a big difference in outcomes. I'm proud to be from a state and local region that are actively involved and planning to make a difference.

4. The Pandemic Influenza patient in PQ or PQC isolation.

a. The general purpose of the Preventive Quarantine approach is to stay healthy, making a sick PIV patient at the PQ a remote possibility. But "stuff happens," so one must be understanding and capable of handling this task.

b. Diagnostic tests will be unnecessary, because the patient's condition and symptoms will make the diagnosis apparent.

High fever, severe body aches, cough, and headache will be difficult to attribute to any other entity during a Pandemic. Significant GI (gastrointestinal) distress could ensue, causing nausea, vomiting, and diarrhea (be cautious of dehydration).

c. The treatment area should be separate from the house or apartment, but could be an isolated room. One should leave the isolation trailer or tent for newcomers vacant, if possible. A newcomer's isolation unit is more likely to be needed than is a room for a Pandemic patient's treatment. The patient room should contain a wash basin and a bucket or similar latrine. Large contamination bags will be needed.

d. The smaller the area, the better. A window and a nonporous floor (easily washed and decontaminated)

would be helpful. A window fan blowing out, creating as much negative pressure in the room as possible, will help reduce contamination of other rooms. A radio and a walkie-talkie on the bed stand would facilitate communication.

e. Outside the door should be new gowns, shower caps, gloves, swim-type goggles, shoe covers (plastic bags secured with rubber bands), and N95 masks (or two tight-fitting surgical masks). Plastic rain gear with separate tops and bottoms could be used for gowns, and then sprayed with 9:1 bleach/water solution after each use. After use, the mask and gloves, shower cap and shoe covers are put in special containers outside the door for later burning. Goggles and gowns must be decontaminated with 9:1 spray and hung to dry. A separate mask might be used over the N95 mask and it destroyed, allowing the N95 mask to be saved for re-use.

f. Undressing from protective garb need to be done in a systematic way, with gloves removed last, after contaminated materials are placed into disposal bags or hung on nails or placed into another container to wash with bleach.

g. Many spray bottles with 9:1 or 5:1 bleach/water solution need to be available by the sick room door and in the room. Start saving the shower spray and window cleaner containers now. Decontaminate everything with spray.

h. The trailer, tent, or isolated room needs to be stocked with everything needed prior to entry, i.e. equipment/medicines/

etc. Food and water are brought each day. Minimal entries and exits should be done. The patient will either live or die here, and should not be allowed to leave the room until they are well. For adults, recovery will take up to 12-14 days. Children remain infectious for a longer period, and need to be isolated for at least 20 days. Between visits, tape the room shut with duct tape, to seal the air spaces as well as possible. The taped door will also act as a reminder of the danger within. (Let the patient know what you are doing, and why you are doing it.)

     i. Patient care while in sick bay.

        i. Tamiflu--give the appropriate recommended dose for 5 days.

        ii. Supply Excedrin and Ibuprofen (such as Motrin) for relief of general discomfort. For adults, two extra-strength Excedrin every 4 hours and 3 Ibuprofen every 8 hours, or similar discomfort medicine measures.

        iii. Keep a supply of masks, hand sanitizer, and gloves available.

        iv. Food and water need to be taken on schedule, like medicine. Eight to sixteen ounces of water every two hours should prevent dehydration. The patient will need to be constantly encouraged and directed.

        v. The patient should be given a perspective on the situation and on how to keep the germ from spreading to others--mask on whenever someone is in the room with them.

        vi. Attempt to make isolation as comfortable as possible, with a radio, television, and telephone. Heating and cooling may be issues, depending on the weather. If wood heat is used, it will need regular attendance.

        vii. A portable waste disposal system should be placed in the room.

viii. A high fever can be regulated in several ways (although a fever may help the body rid itself of the virus). Acetaminophen/ibuprofen, lukewarm sponge baths, a fan, or a light blanket when chilled, can all contribute to patient comfort.

ix. If breathing becomes more and more difficult and the patient gets more and more sick within the first few days, these could be ominous signs of the influenza's progression. There are really only comfort measures to be taken here. The leader needs to assess the situation for transfer to a hospital for possible advanced care. Communication with the outside medical care system will quickly give an answer as to the advisability of transfer. Depending on many factors and the severity of the Pandemic, the possibility of death within the PQ facility exists. Outside health care providers can be helpful answering questions via telephone about general care measures.

x. If the patient does not exhibit worsening or serious problems in the first 4-5 days of illness, and now begins to improve somewhat, the patient may be given antibiotics from the prescription medical kit, to prevent a secondary pneumonia. A telephone consultation with a health care provider may be needed to help make the decision. Secondary bacterial pneumonias may not be as common as we once thought. Depending on the patient's previous health, the course of recovery may be complicated by other health issues, such as a heart or kidney problem. If at 7-10 days the patient is in the recovery mode and the chicken soup has worked its magic, the patient can still be shedding virus. This is especially true of children, who can shed for a total of 20-plus days.

xi. The recovered patient will be invaluable to the system, because they will have resistance to any further cyclic recurrence of the PIV. They can leave the PQ at will, but could be fomite carriers and care should be taken accordingly.

xii. Since fevers, nausea/vomiting and diarrhea could complicate patient recovery, IV fluids and the equipment to start an intravenous line could be helpful. If there is no medical person in the PQC, the leader may attend a demonstration of a few of these skills with a health care provider during the preplanning phase, or he may get directions over the telephone. We do CPR direction over the phone; we could just as well describe other skills. Skills could be broadened to include Automatic Defibrillator Training, etc., if equipment is available.

5. Dealing with emotional issues.

   a. Problems could be significant at the PQ; problems could be catastrophic in the outside PQ environment. Plan on having issues involving:

    i. Children.

    ii. Adolescents.

    iii. Situational and seasonal depressions.

    iv. Guilt for being in a better situation than the rest of the world.

    v. Anger at being in a controlled environment, with restrictions.

    vi. Death and dying/dealing with grief.

    vii. Funeral issues/grave sites (due to differences between what was expected and what needs to be done).

   b. There may be emotionally distraught people that could be dangerous, and they could be at the door.

There will always be the usual criminally disturbed elements. Need we return to an Old West mentality? The situation and our value system will determine our responses.

E. Sentinel event examples for PQ exit.

Sentinel events for exit are difficult to choose before the Pandemic starts, since variables may shift timing. For increased risk reduction, plan on a timeframe between 6-12 months.

1. Announcement by CDC or local health authorities of a significant decline in the number of new cases of PIV in your area.

2. Announcement by CDC or WHO of a significant decline in new cases of PIV in the United States.

3. Failure of a new wave of PIV to materialize.

(It's probably safe if no new wave in six to eight months from #1 or #2 above.) There may still be lingering PIV cases around the world, and another wave could come later.

4. Removal of all restrictive rules regarding travel, or social interactions by CDC or local health authorities, if such rules had been instituted.

5. Availability of PIV-specific vaccination program that would be available to you and your family.

6. Announcement from CDC or local health authorities of NO new cases of PIV in your region in the past three to six months.

7. Announcement of NO new cases of PIV in the United States in the past three to six months.

8. WHO and/or CDC announces that the Pandemic is over.

9. The predetermined and agreed upon time established for PQ exit is met, regardless of events. (Perhaps determined by food supplies or similar.)

VI. REFERENCES

(These are not necessarily in true bibliography form, but should be enough for you to locate the information.)

A. General books.

1. The Great Influenza by John M. Barry. Great reading about the devastation of the 1918 Pandemic.

2. Crisis Preparedness Handbook by Jack A. Spigarelli (updated 2nd edition). List of good general reference books on country living.

3. Wilderness Medicine by William Forgey, M.D.

4. Camping & Cooking With the Bare Essentials by Tony Kellar.

5. Outward Bound Wilderness First Aid Handbook, Issac & Goth.

6. Wilderness Medicine, Management of Wilderness and Environmental Emergencies by Auerbach.

7. Mayo Clinic Family Health Book (3rd edition).

8. Merck Manual. Medical book.

9. The Good Life by Scott and Helen Nearing.

10. Guidelines CPR 2005 (www.americanheart.org/cpr).

B. Catalogues

(Most on web sites now).

    1. Survival Unlimited.com--new lamp burns any fuel brightly and safely. Petromax lamp (isopropyl alcohol, can be used indoors without odor or danger from fumes).

    2. Lehman's non-Electric Catalogue, www.lehmans.com--sustainable equipment.

    3. Sources Directory Chapter 32 Crisis Preparedness Handbook, by Spigarelli (updated 2nd edition). Almost every source you could ever use.

C. Key articles.

Most in web sites of Pandemicflu.gov or www.who.int.

Would like to mention the classic work that changed the mood of everyone in the scientific community to one of extreme caution. The researchers were able to resurrect the H1N1 virus from the 1918 Pandemic, by exhuming corpses in the Alaskan permafrost. They found that H5N1 is following the course that the very serious H1N1 followed, and not the less severe courses of 1957 and 1968.

    1. Journal of Clinical Virology, September 2005, Jeff Taubenberger, etal, from the Institute of Pathology/CDC/Mt. Sinai School of Medicine.

    2. 2nd Reconstruction 1918 Spanish Influenza Pandemic Virus, October 7 Science.

    3. An Investors Guide to Avian Flu, by Sherry Cooper and Don Coxe. A Special Report, August, 2005. A BMO Nesbitt Burns production.

D. Official sources of information.

1. __Hotline to CDC 24/7, 1-800-CDC-INFO or 1-800-232-4636

2. __E-mail inquiry @ cdc.gov

3. __www.pandemicflu.gov

4. __Links to any State's Department of Health can be found at www.pandemicflu.gov

5. __www.who.int

6. __www.cdc.gov

E. Web sites to know.

1. __www.providentliving.org--Web site of the Latter Day Saints (Mormon), information on sustainable living.

2. __www.bird-flu-influenza.com--Steven Jones, Australian biologist.

3. __www.recombinomics.com--latest information on H5N1 mutations.

4. __www.fema.gov/kids--emergency management web site for kids.

F. Stores selling bulk foods.

1. __Sam's Club--for bulk foods and large-amount product purchases.

2. __Feed stores--good for many bulk products.

3. __Organic food stores--good for many bulk products.

G. Financial resources.

1. __www.boothfinancialadvisors.com--Booth Financial Advisors, Saginaw, MN (Jim Booth)--understands the Pandemic and all of its ramifications. 218-279-6005.

2. __sherry.cooper@bmonb.com--The Avian Flu Crisis,

An Economic Update (Special Report 2006), Dr. Sherry Cooper, BMO--Nesbitt Burns.

3. __Emergency Financial First Aid Kit, developed by Operation Hope, FEMA and Citizens Corp.